Lou Ferrigno's Guide to Personal Power, Bodybuilding, and Fitness

LOU FERRIGNO'S

GUIDE TO

PERSONAL POWER,

BODYBUILDING,

AND FITNESS

Library of Congress Cataloging-in-Publication Data

Ferrigno, Lou.
    Lou Ferrigno's guide to personal power, bodybuilding, and fitness /
Lou Ferrigno : forewords by Anthony Robbins and Joe Weider.
       p.   cm.
   ISBN 0-8092-3125-5
    1. Ferrigno, Lou.   2. Bodybuilders—United States—Biography.
3. Bodybuilding.   4. Physical Fitness   I. Title
GV545.52.F47A3   1996
646.7′5′092—dc20
[B]   96-15171
                                         CIP

Cover design by Todd Petersen
Cover photo by Art Zeller
Interior photos by Chris Lund, Ralph DeHaan, Robert Reiff, Art Zeller, and Paula Crane
Interior design by Hespenheide Design

Manufactured in the United States of America

To my beautiful wife, Carla,
and my three lovely children—
Shanna, Louie, and Brent

CONTENTS

FOREWORD

I've known Lou Ferrigno for several years, and I've always had tremendous admiration and respect for the man. While this may surprise you, it isn't his physique that impresses me most. What sets him apart is his ability to persevere and overcome adversity, and continue to establish new standards—not only for the sport of bodybuilding, but also for every other endeavor to which he commits himself.

Lou has been faced with hardships of a kind that many of us can't even imagine. Yet, he overcame them and became phenomenally successful. The reason? His decision to unleash what I call his "personal power." He refuses to give in to obstacles and views them merely as challenges along life's path. His success over the years is a living illustration of a core belief shared by every leader I've ever known: "There's always a way . . . if I'm committed."

While Lou's accomplishments in the area of physical mastery are legendary, I am even more inspired by his dedication to educating and influencing others in a positive way. Lou Ferrigno is a champion of the human spirit who shows us what is possible, and I am proud to call him my friend.

—Anthony Robbins,
bestselling author
(*Giant Steps,
Awaken the Giant
Within*, and *Unlimited
Power*)

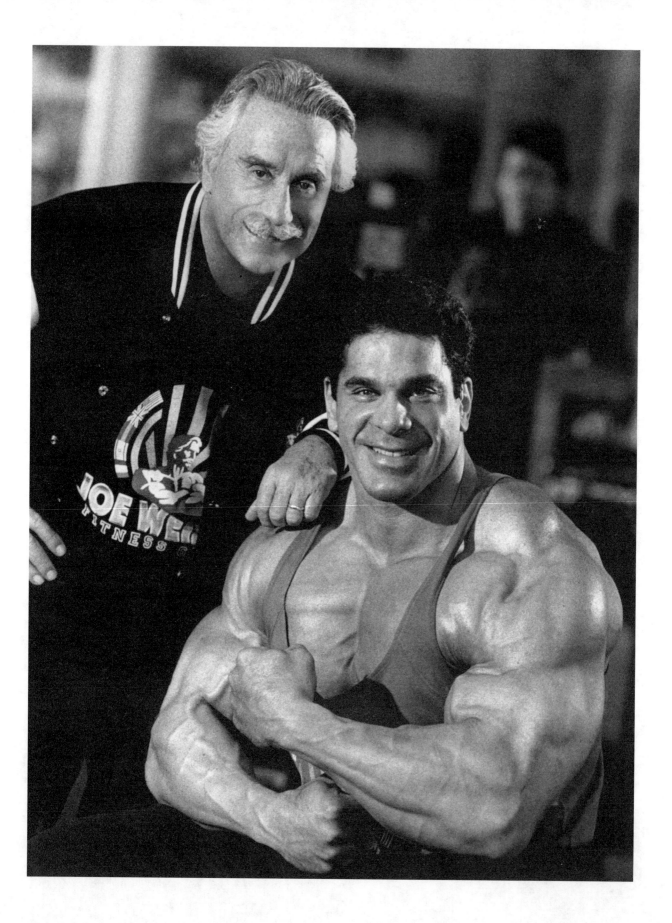

FOREWORD

It's safe to say that at a body weight that fluctuates between 290 and 310 pounds of grade-A muscle and standing 6'5", Lou Ferrigno, for pure size, has no peer in the bodybuilding world. With 23" arms and a 34" waist, his structure, proportion, and muscularity come close to perfection. The superhuman image he conveys on movie and television screens (and enjoys in the bodybuilding world) is an awesome sight to behold in person.

As you're no doubt aware, Lou starred in the spectacular television series *The Incredible Hulk*, in which his truly incredible physique has been seen by millions of astounded television viewers, and which did much to promote the sport of bodybuilding to mainstream America.

To me (and it's by no means a solitary opinion) Lou represents all that is good and possible with bodybuilding. He's a decent man with good morals, solid principles, and a sterling character, and he's one of the most dedicated athletes I've ever known.

His dedication has paid off handsomely for Lou, as he's competed successfully in many sports from football to cycling, proving himself to be an excellent all-round athlete.

The one thing that Louie has always coveted but that, so far, has managed to elude his grasp, is the Joe Weider's Mr. Olympia title. He took a run at it in 1975, losing out to the then-invincible Arnold Schwarzenegger. He then returned to competition after a layoff of some 17 years—at age 40!—to wow all in attendance with his incredible muscularity. He even competed in the Olympia the following year and, as always, was the favorite of the fans.

Lou never ceases to amaze me, not only in his muscle development (which is just a small portion of the man) but also in the way he deals with adversity. Lou has overcome handicaps and problems that would leave most people reeling on life's ropes. How he overcame these obstacles and built one of the greatest physiques of all time has been print-worthy for decades. I'm glad he's committing his amazing personal power and bodybuilding philosophy to paper.

—Joe Weider,
the "Master Blaster"

ACKNOWLEDGMENTS

Many people helped get this book on its feet. I dedicate it first and foremost, and with the deepest love and affection, to my wife, Carla May, my beautiful daughter, Shanna, and my two sons, Lou and Brent. This book would not have been possible without the inspiration and strength given me by my family and friends.

I'd also like to thank Joe Weider, the Trainer of Champions. I wouldn't be here today without Joe Weider's guidance, help, support, respect, and love.

My thanks also to Ben Weider, who's made bodybuilding a major mainstream event.

Also due thanks is my good friend Art Zeller, who has photographed me for the last 20 years and always brought out the best my physique had to offer. Artie is the best artistic photographer in the sport of bodybuilding.

I'd additionally like to thank my friends at *FLEX* magazine for all of their help in this project: John Little, Martin Withrow for his work in layout and design, George DePirro for editing the finished manuscript, and, of course, *FLEX* Editor-in-Chief Jerry Kindela, for all of his input and understanding.

And finally, I would like to thank Chris Lund, Ralph DeHaan, Robert Reiff, Ken Marcus, and Paula Crane for their photographic excellence, the proof of which can be seen throughout the pages of this book.

Without the support and encouragement of all of the above, this book would never have come about.

—Lou Ferrigno

FACT SHEET

Childhood

- Date of birth: November 9, 1951.
- Lou's earliest home gym, located in the basement, included a crude lat machine, an adjustable bench with stands, squat stands, and, of course, free weights, some of which his father, Matty, had been using since before Lou was born.
- Lou has a younger brother, Andrew, and a younger sister, Lisa.
- As a newborn, Lou suffered a series of ear infections that left him with an 80 percent hearing loss.
- Lou attended St. Athanasius Elementary School, located at Bay Parkway and 51st Street in Brooklyn. Also, three times a week, he attended classes held by the New York League for the Hard of Hearing. At age 16 (1966), he began attending Brooklyn Technical High School.

Body Talk

- Lou's first physique contest was the Mr. New Jersey Open Hercules held in Trenton. He took 22nd place. The Open Hercules was held in March 1971, the year of Lou's first major physique win, the WBBG (World Body Building Guild) Teen-Age Eastern America. Thereafter, he accrued the following record:

1971	WBBG Teen-Age Mr. America
1972	WBBG Mr. America—2nd place
1973	IFBB Mr. America
1973	IFBB (International Federation of Body Building) Mr. Universe
1974	IFBB Mr. International
1974	IFBB Mr. Universe
1974	Mr. Olympia—2nd place (winner: Arnold Schwarzenegger)
1975	Mr. Olympia—3rd place (winner: Arnold Schwarzenegger)
1976	ABC-Superstars Competition—4th place
1976	Tried out and played for the Toronto Argonauts (Canadian Football League)

1977   World's Strongest Man Competition—
       4th place
- Lou returned to competitive bodybuilding in
  1992 (at 40 years of age!) after a 17-year
  absence and placed 12th at the Mr. Olympia
  contest, held in Helsinki, Finland. He entered
  again one year later and moved up to 10th
  (Dorian Yates won both shows).

Stage and Screen

- **Television**: *The Incredible Hulk* (March10,
  1978–June 2, 1982), *Trauma Center* September
  22, 1983–December 8, 1983), *Incredible Hulk*
  made-for-TV movies (1986,1987, 1988),
  Incredible Hulk cartoon show (voice; airing
  fall 1996 on UPN), frequent talk-show
  appearances, has a recurring role on the sitcom
  The King of Queens.

- **Film:** *Hercules, Hercules II, Scavenger 2,000,
  All's Fair, The Seven Magnificent Gladiators,
  Sinbad, Cage, Cage II, The Misery Brothers,
  Stand Tall* (a soon to be released autobio-
  graphical documentary), cameo appearance in
  the new *Incredible Hulk Movie* directed by
  Ann Lee.
- **Stage:** *Arsenic and Old Lace, Of Mice and Men,
  Requiem for a Heavyweight.*

Family

- Lou wed Carla Green on May 3, 1980. They
  have three children: Shanna Victoria, Lou Jr.,
  and Brent.
  (Material courtesy of *FLEX* magazine and Joe
  Roark, IFBB Men's Historian.)

Lou Ferrigno's Guide to Personal Power, Bodybuilding, and Fitness

Part I

Lou's Story

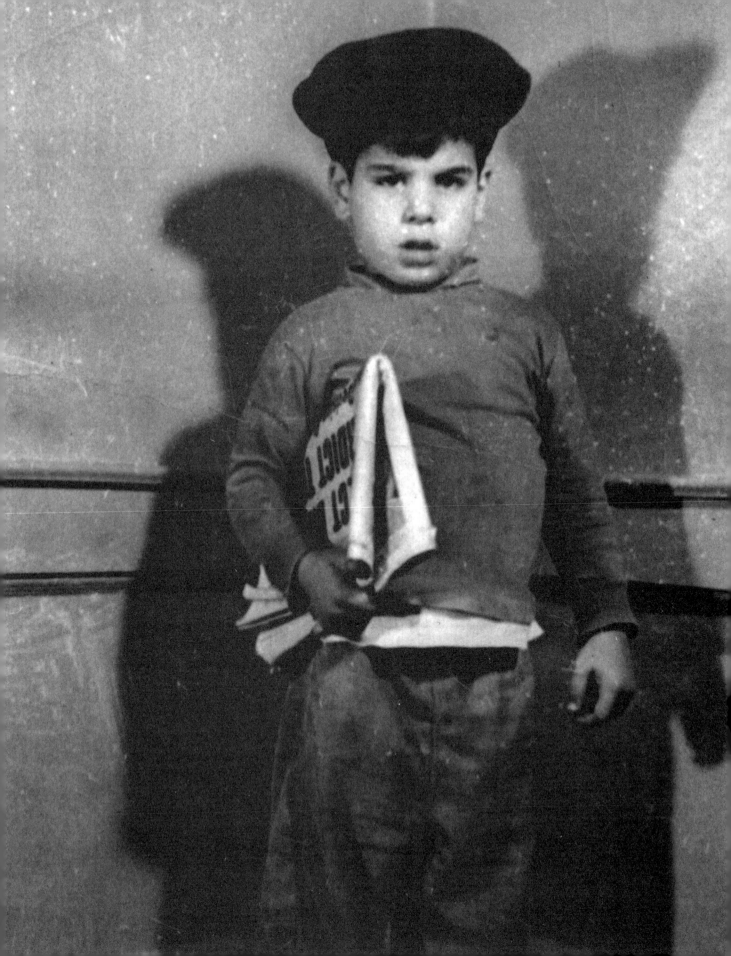

1
How It All Began

I have a very vivid recollection from my childhood. It consists of me at five years of age running down a hospital corridor frantically trying to find my parents. Tears are streaming down my cheeks, and my voice is hoarse from screaming out their names. I push my way through two heavy swinging steel doors, and there, 20 yards before me, are my mother and father. I run to them and grab hold of my father's leg, still crying and scared but momentarily relieved in having finally located them. I look up at my dad, longing to see a paternal smile of reassurance, but instead I'm greeted with an expression of disdain—a sort of "how could you embarrass me like this?" look. It hits me like a kick in the stomach; after all, to me at age five, my father is my god—my source of self-esteem and, together with my mother, my sole sounding board to reality.

The prospect of being left alone in a hospital with a strange man in a white jacket who informed me that he was going to cut into my throat and remove my tonsils terrified me. "What if I lose my ability to speak—the way I've lost my ability to hear?" I ask myself. That would mean only more rejection, and I couldn't live with that. Still, there was no empathy forthcoming from my dad, only a look of disgust that I would never, despite my future successes, be able to either forget or shake loose from my consciousness.

It would be nice to conclude this story by tacking on a happy ending such as "And then I woke up in my bed, and my parents were right there by my bedside, reassuring me that I'd had a terrible nightmare." Unfortunately, my early childhood experiences, of which this was but one, weren't dreams from which I had only to awake in order to escape. They were real experiences—all too real in some instances—but they did ultimately serve to mold my character and values as I grew older.

My having mentioned this is not to suggest that I didn't get along with my parents, as I was always close to my mom, but Dad was a different story entirely. Things were never rosy between us. In fact, they weren't ever normal in the sense of the typical father/son relationship that most young boys share with their fathers. I can partly explain it by the fact that in many ways my father and I had the same temperament, and individuals of like charges and temperaments often tend to repel one another. Whatever the reason, my dad was at times my strongest defender and always my worst critic—sometimes bordering on wanton cruelty.

Something I've learned, not only from professional psychologists and books but also from personal experience with my own children, is that kids are not equipped with the psychological tools to defend themselves from ridicule, scorn, or insults from their parents. I was struck by a passage from a story I read by Mark Twain: "It's a shameful thing to insult a little child. It has its feelings, it has its small dignity; and since it cannot defend them, it is surely an ignoble act to injure them" ("Which Was the Dream?"—1897). It is a line that could have been applied directly to my father.

An Early Dose of Reality

I grew up in Brooklyn, where my father was a lieutenant in the police force. I had two siblings: a brother, Andrew, and a sister, Lisa. Being a policeman, Dad was exposed to many unsettling and painful experiences every day, and out of necessity to survive with his psyche intact, he developed a callous perspective on life.

To his consternation, his kids, who were not exposed to the dregs of society on a daily basis, didn't share his gloom-and-doom outlook. Hell, we even held the "infantile" belief that life could be good and (dare say!) enjoyable, given the right vocational pursuits. To Dad, however, this was a pipe dream; the reality of the world was that everyone was out to screw one another out of something or bash their brains out at the first opportunity. To him, you were either tough and pessimistic or a victim and a rube.

And so he was absolutely mortified when it was discovered that his number-one son had been born "defective," the result of a severe inner-ear infection that had gone undetected until 80 percent of his hearing was totally obliterated. Suddenly, the advocate of anticipating every contingency and being able to respond to anything had sired a problem for which he was totally unprepared: a boy who had the deck stacked against him and had taken a major stum-ble on the road of life coming right out of the gate.

"What did I do to deserve this?" thought my father. "Like my life isn't complicated enough with the meager salary my ass-busting job on the force provides and having to pay rent, provide for my wife, and now a son who will require God knows how much medical attention just to break even!" Surely, the gods were punishing Matty Ferrigno for something. Or at least, so thought my father back in 1953.

Despite this attitude, which he didn't always opt to conceal, my father remained my hero, my giant, and, to a very large extent, my role model. He was big (or so he appeared to me during my adolescence, at least), and he had a great physique, with broad shoulders, thick arms, a sweep to his quads, and full, squared pecs. He looked to me like Steve Reeves, the star of the first Hercules films. On one memorable day Dad walked out of the shower with a towel wrapped around his waist and came into the kitchen; he looked so incredible that I just sat there with my eyes riveted to his physique. Taking note of his impact, he smirked at me and said, "Hey, Louie, watch this!" Then he hit a double-biceps pose, and his biceps jutted straight up into the air like miniature Mount Kilimanjaros! My jaw hit the ground. Then, with a laugh, he turned on his heel and went back into the bathroom. That was probably the first time that I saw what could be accomplished with the human body when you refuse to let yourself go, as many of my friends' parents did who had reached my father's age.

Another time, I'd just gotten a new bicycle from my grandfather, and several neighborhood toughs had encircled me and were pushing and punching me, trying to get me to let go of my prized possession. Suddenly, they froze. Noticing that the rain of blows had subsided, I looked up, and there was Dad in a skintight T-shirt walking down the stairs of the tenement house where we lived. "Hey, what d'ya think you're doing to my kid?" he queried, his voice stern and direct. "Do you think you can push my kid around because he has a hearing problem?"

He was growing angrier by the second. One of the kids piped up, "You don't frighten me. If you do anything, I'll tell my dad and he'll sue your ass!" My father's eyes lit up at that. "Oh, yeah?" he responded. "You go get your old man and I'll beat the shit out of him too!" With that, all of them took off—and they were legitimately scared. I don't remember a time when I was ever prouder of my old man. He actually stood up for me. He had shown me, not just in words but in deed, that he actually cared for me and about me, that he would protect me if he felt I needed it, and that he cared enough about me to do it. Although he never told me that he loved me, that was the closest thing to it that I ever felt from him. And, for the time being, that was enough to get me by.

My mother, on the other hand, was like most Italian mothers—only a lot more special. She would always look out for "my boy" and made sure that I ate adequately and provided plenty of encouragement. Unfortunately, my father perceived this care to be at the expense of attention that should have been devoted to him, and friction would develop as soon as he returned home from work—friction to the point where Mom would express her love and concern for any of her children only when Dad wasn't around. When he was in the house, she simply mirrored his attitude toward me and the other children in order to dodge a fight. My brother and sister never encountered problems with this on the order that I did mainly because they were willing to go along with most edicts my dad delivered. I was always more of a rebel, not in the James Dean sense of the term, but just more independent-minded. I put a lot of stock in my own capacity to reason and judge things, largely because I spent a great deal of time on my own.

In Search of Ideals

My hearing loss had affected me socially once I reached the age to become aware of my affliction, and I became very reluctant to speak with people. Like that of most other people with a hearing disorder, my speech was somewhat difficult to understand, and it would always register shock on the faces of people who initiated a conversation with me for the first time. Kids, being kids, called me names such as "Deaf Louie," which only served to lower my already rapidly depreciating self-esteem. As a result, I opted to avoid all possible embarrassment by keeping to myself as much as I could.

When hearing isn't one of your strong suits, you tend to focus your recreational pursuits in the direction of one of the more potent senses that remain. In my case, this turned out to be a visual medium, and reading became my passion—not just classical literature or novels, which didn't stimulate me at all, but more so comic books, with their romantic portrayals of heroes, of a world where good could indeed triumph over evil, where crime ultimately didn't pay, and where people existed who truly cared about justice and being decent to one another.

I was always an action fan. Pictures served to stimulate me, and I became a latter-day Walter Mitty, envisioning myself in all sorts of incredible adventures, possessed of extraordinary strength and physique, and able to help others in distress. Coincidentally, one of the comic books I enjoyed the most was Marvel Comics' *The Incredible Hulk*. I empathized with the plight of the man/monster who didn't want to hurt anybody and just wanted to be left alone to live his life. I understood his anger and reveled in his power and strength and the way that his tormentors would ultimately bow down before him when he eventually lost his temper. The Hulk was cool.

But reality always brought me back from my fantasy dreamworld. Every morning, I'd awaken to discover that I wasn't the Hulk or a superhero but merely a handicapped human being, and my handicap was broadcast to everyone with eyes, owing to the cumbersome wire and ill-fitting earpiece with which I had to be fitted. Hearing

aids in those days weren't as sophisticated as they've since become. They consisted of a large box that had to be strapped to your chest, with a wire that extended out of your shirt collar and into a large piece of semi-molded plastic that served as the earpiece. I thought I looked like a Martian or, at the very least, a freak. I felt sad and lost and wanted to cry every time my mother would put my hearing aid on me. Sometimes she'd cry herself.

My classmates were quick to taunt me. "Here comes Tin-Ear!" "Hey, let's swear at him behind his back—he won't know what we're saying. We can say anything!" And the ever-popular "Deaf Louie" and "Hey, Deaf and Dumb!"

This last tag cut deep. When you're young it's hard to learn that the terms *deaf* and *dumb* are not attached like boxcars. Fearing similar reactions on all sides, I would deliberately seek out a chair in the classroom that was near the back of the room and would turn my head so that the teacher wouldn't be able to see my hearing aid. This way, I reasoned, she wouldn't call attention to my impediment and thereby tip off the other students who might not have been aware of it. I thought this was a pretty sound strategy at the time. Unfortunately, such a tactic also put me way out of range to lip-read with any effectiveness, with the result that I couldn't make out a word of what the teacher was saying and my grades, correspondingly, took a nosedive. This served only to underscore the notion that I was indeed "dumb" as well as "deaf."

My mother had to be notified of my failing grades, which, of course, meant that my father would be informed of the situation as well. My poor academic performance just added to my father's inherent belief that he'd brought a complete screw-up into the world, which compelled him to tell me, repeatedly, just how "disappointed" he was with me.

One particular evening my father, at my mother's insistence, sat me down with the stated intention of "helping" me learn to read in order to save me from further embarrassment during school reading assignments. He asked me to read out loud. As I struggled with each word, I looked to him with hope, wanting some sign of encouragement that I was doing okay. Instead, he just rolled his eyes, rose from his chair, and walked away. He passed my mother in the doorway and, turning to her, said, "He's never going to be a normal person as an adult." It was a black day for me, as I lacked the confidence and knowledge to deal with the pain and humiliation to which I was subjected. I often cried myself to sleep back then out of the increasing sense of hopelessness that my father's constant berating was starting to instill in my young view of life.

Still, my father was my hero, and I wanted to be just like him. And, of course, I decided I would become a policeman. I started to lift weights and become stronger. Instead of occupying my thoughts with superheroes and comic books, I now began to daydream about being Lou Ferrigno, Matty's son, a policeman so good that even my father would respect me by virtue of my devotion to duty and the numerous citations I would work hard to receive. I loved the idea of wearing that distinctive blue policeman's uniform and having people envy and respect me—that and, of course, being able to wear a gun! I mean, that would be the nearest thing to being a cowboy that I could imagine! Yes, sir, I was going to be the best policeman I possibly could—that was going to be my future, just like my dad! That is, until the day I screwed up the courage to tell him of my dream over breakfast and he shot it out of the sky with one tersely worded sentence: "The police department will never take a deaf kid onto the force."

At that moment I felt ashamed, emasculated, humiliated, and anything and everything else that indicates a complete loss of self-respect and self-esteem. I'd thought that, if I wasn't like the other kids, I could at least be like my dad. After all, even though I screwed up by being born with a hearing problem, we still shared the same bloodline. My dad had respect and admiration, so at least genetics held forth the possibility for me to one day do the same. Now even that hope had been dashed against the rocks of my father's reality. He had told me with that one sentence not only that I didn't measure up at school or with other kids but that I didn't measure up *period*. Then, for good measure, he tossed a little more fuel on the fire by adding, "The cops won't take you; the fire department won't take you. The only thing you'll be able to do is drive a cab." Again I felt that sickening sensation in the pit of my stomach. I wanted to scream at him, "You're wrong! I can be successful! I can measure up and be respected!" but I was too browbeaten to believe it at that point and far too scared of what he'd do to me if I attempted to express such a sentiment.

Instead, I took it. I took all that he had to dish out that morning. After all, that's what life was all about, according to my father: being able to "take it." When he was finished, I excused myself from the table, gathered up my books, and tried to stop the cascade of tears flowing down my cheeks before I got to school where the other kids would see me and have something else to ridicule me for. It was, at that point, the toughest day of my life.

2
The Turning Point

Given my problems at home, I was somewhat surprised to learn that I did have some value as a person in terms of athletics. This revelation may seem obvious to those who have seen me compete as an adult in the Canadian Football League, the "Superstars" athletic competition, or the "World's Strongest Man" events, but back in the mid-1960s, you would have been as surprised as I was by the discovery.

I'd always enjoyed playing stickball in and around the streets of Brooklyn while I was growing up. Stickball is like baseball, only you play in the streets (as opposed to a ball diamond) and use a stick (either a broom handle or a sawed-off hockey stick) and try your hardest to whack that ball as far down the road as possible. It was a popular pastime in Brooklyn, and I remember the old men sitting out on their balconies as if they were witnessing a World Series and cheering on the local stickball "hitters."

Almost from the start, I got the reputation of being "a hitter"—that is, a guy who could really tag any pitch that came my way and send it into orbit. Whenever I'd come up to hit, all the guys in the outfield would scurry back as far as they could to attempt to corral one of my smacks. They seldom did. This gave me an incredible

surge of self-esteem that had been denied in so many other areas of my life.

I became more confident in my athletic ability and, to my surprise, popular among my peers for stickball, which, in turn, led to my being recruited for Little League. I enjoyed baseball and was assigned to play first base and actually was good at it. But my real talent was hitting! I think I became proficient in hitting because of my hearing impairment. I honestly believe that it caused me to hyperdevelop most of my other senses, and naturally, sight was one of them. I could see every pitch that came my way, with the result that very seldom did one go by me.

I should mention that if I had any "natural" athletic ability, I came by it as a result of my father. He was an exceptional athlete, so I have a genetic disposition toward being at least moderately successful in athletics. Ironically, whenever my father would come to see me play in Little League, I would invariably have a terrible game. I would tense up, sweat, and be so nervous— because I knew that he was watching and just waiting to criticize me for something—that I would try too hard and always perform badly. I just couldn't focus properly on the task at hand. Whenever a pitch would blow by me for a third strike, I'd look over at my dad, and he'd just shake his head in disgust. "You'll never make it as an athlete," he'd tell me afterward, and then he'd go on about how, if he were playing, he would have smacked every one of those pitches out of the park. I'd just nod in agreement, hoping that by doing so I could keep him off the more painful topic of how inept he thought I was.

Thinking "Big"

It was about this time that I was walking through the kitchen one day and noticed my dad looking intently at a picture in a magazine. Not used to seeing anything that would keep him riveted like that, I came closer to see what it was. It turned out to be a photograph of former movie Tarzan Johnny Weissmuller. "Gee, would you look at the physique on that guy, Louie," my father commented. "Now, that is a well-built guy!" Weissmuller, who was shirtless, displayed a broad-shouldered, rugged look, and there was no disputing the fact that he was very well built indeed. "That's a real man's body," my dad said wistfully and then left the room. I liked the look that Weissmuller exuded, not unlike the rugged looks of the superheroes who adorned the covers of my comic books in those days. I remembered his image for a long time afterward.

The next time I saw a physique that resembled Weissmuller's was when I attended a special summer camp and witnessed one of the counselors working out. He was a bodybuilder, and his arms and pecs were incredible! I used to forgo a lot of the typical camping amusements and pastimes just to go down to his cabin and watch him work out. Picking up on my interest, he showed me a few exercises and how to perform them properly. Then he told me about bodybuilding and that it required tremendous dedication, but if you were willing to apply yourself, you could literally transform yourself into a superman. Even as a youngster with an 80 percent hearing loss, I was "all ears" when he said that!

I well remember the first time I picked up a barbell: the feel of the cold steel in my hands and the firm but gentle pull on my biceps that shook and quivered like Elvis Presley's legs during his heyday as I slowly contracted my muscles against the resistance. It was "love at first sight." I knew at that moment that when I returned home from summer camp I was going to be using my father's old barbell set (which had been gathering dust in the basement for as long as I could remember) in a way that it had never been used before.

I vaguely recall my dad working out as I was growing up, but it mainly consisted of attaching

a barbell plate to a towel and then placing one end of the towel over his head in order to perform neck exercises. My intentions were to go way beyond the merely rehabilitative; I wanted to be both strong and admired like my heroes from the comic books and, more recently, in the muscle magazines. Above all else, I wanted to be "big."

I came upon my first muscle magazine innocently enough: One day I was browsing at a secondhand magazine store, and there on the cover of one of the magazines was a bodybuilder named Steve Reeves. I did a double take. The man looked incredible (to this day, Steve Reeves has my all-time favorite physique) with huge broad shoulders, thick pecs and arms, and a tremendous V-shaped back that tapered down into a waist so thin, even a hornet would have been envious. I offered the shopkeeper four of my comic books in exchange for the magazine. He accepted, and a deal was struck. Coincidentally, that same night a Steve Reeves Hercules movie was playing on the late show on television, and it blew me away. His muscles moved and twitched like the shoulders of a Clydesdale, and he carried himself with real poise and power.

I read, reread, and reread again the muscle magazine I'd bartered for and worked out that night with a renewed sense of purpose. I awoke the next morning with a ravenous appetite—not for food, but for knowledge! I wanted more information on building muscles and developing a physique like that of my new hero, Steve Reeves! I hurried down to the magazine store and worked out a deal with the owner to continue to trade him comic books for muscle magazines. As soon as I got a "new" issue, I'd run home with it and go into my room and read it. I'd pore over each issue as though it had been written just for me. And I'd learn more and more about how my body functioned, which exercises affected which body parts, and all the "hows" and "whys" of training for size and power.

I found an old mirror in the basement. It had a large crack running through the length of it, but it served my purposes perfectly. Within a

matter of months, I had built other pieces of equipment that I'd read about in the magazines until I had fashioned a fairly respectable home gym. I'd work out seven days a week and perform as many exercises as I could in an effort to really build big and powerful muscles.

One day, in exchange for helping him paint the house that summer, my dad offered to drive me down to Joe Weider's store to buy a bench press and some additional weights. I couldn't wait to get there. After all, this was Joe Weider's store! Joe Weider—the man who owned and published both *Muscle Builder* and *Mr. America* magazines! The man who had trained every single bodybuilding champion since 1946—including Steve Reeves! My heart was racing, and it seemed to take forever to get to our destination. We finally pulled into the parking lot, and I beheld for the first time the building that was to become my personal mecca.

Once inside, I was amazed at all of the equipment that was actually available for bodybuilders. Instantly, I had another daydream of how all of this equipment would look in my own home gym. Man, let me tell you, seeing that image and how that equipment could contribute to my bodybuilding gains fired me up for several weeks. I picked out a good bench press along with a pair of 50-pound plates and a pair of 35s. My dad went inside to pay for the plates while I loaded them into the trunk of our car. Realizing I couldn't be seen, I had what is probably a typically adolescent reaction: "Why not keep loading more plates into the trunk?" I did so unseen, and when I was through, the gas tank from my father's Oldsmobile was so low it was touching the springs! When we got home and popped the trunk, Dad saw the additional plates acquired at a "five-finger discount," and he hit the roof. He shouted, "I'm a cop, Louie. I arrest people for this very thing!"

At that moment for the first time I felt some empathy with people who steal to support their addictions. The truth was that I was addicted—to pumping iron. I would have done anything to get bigger and stronger. However, I was not

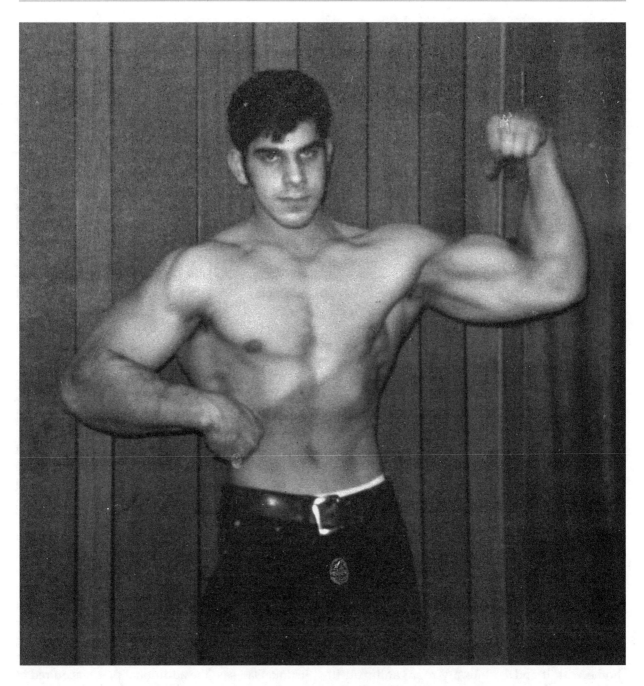

without some sense of morality, and I knew that I had just committed a terrible wrong. I fully expected to be severely reprimanded, grounded, and made to sheep-facedly return the merchandise to Joe Weider's store. Worse yet, many of Joe's champions who were featured in his magazines each month worked there, men such as Harold Poole and Bill Grant. They would know that I stole the weights, that I was a "thief" and had brought shame upon my family. I was prepared for all of this—but then my dad just smiled and walked inside. The weights stayed.

A funny feeling developed inside of me when this happened. Although I was the one who had committed the misdeed, my feeling was one of disrespect creeping in toward my father. I knew that what I'd done was wrong and that I should be made to atone. However, once it was discovered, it was quickly and deliberately forgotten. I later returned the weights myself.

Firing Up the Will

Despite such temporary lapses in ethical matters, I never let up in my training. There's something to be said for being cognizant of having brought about changes through applied reason. For one thing, it reveals to you that, despite what others may say or think, you do possess the capacity to make things happen. A line spoken in a Bruce Lee movie exemplifies my point: "We are unique gentlemen, in that we create ourselves. Through long years of rigorous training, we forge our bodies in the fires of our will." Although the comment refers to martial artists, it could be applied with equal validity to bodybuilders.

I noticed that, slowly but steadily to be sure, my self-confidence was beginning to increase. After all, I had learned something of significance about anatomy, physiology, and kinesiology, subjects about which I'd never have learned anything—at least not in any practical context—in high school. I saw how I could improve my physique, and then I busily mapped out a program that would bring about these alterations. And, more to the point, I was successful at what I did—and there's no greater confidence builder than being successful.

Members of my family as well as people at school had noticed that my body was changing and with it, the way I comported myself and expressed my opinions. No longer was I the wallflower. I actually thought that my opinions should carry some weight; after all, they were no longer the empty-headed babblings of some "deaf and dumb" child. These were the carefully considered opinions of a guy who got things done, of a young man who was "diligent," never

missed a workout; "tenacious," who would fight through the pain of adversity seven days a week, rain or shine; "practical," who would determine what body parts needed the most work and then modify his training schedule to hit those parts exclusively; and "successful," who desired to bring about positive change and then single-handedly made it happen. Here was a young man who looked better as a result and was far stronger and healthier. This, in essence, was a new Lou Ferrigno!

Soon I was able to add more equipment to my home gym. Quick to arrive were a vertical leg-press machine, various dumbbells, and—my favorite—a lat machine! Not a professional lat machine made with the proper bushings, high-tension cables, and heavy-duty steel construction so much as a lat bar connected to two high pulleys by a length of cable that attached to a bar that held weights. However, to me, this lat machine was "it." And, truth be told, I had some of my best back workouts ever with that machine!

As my body started to develop and my confidence began to bloom, I became a zealot for bodybuilding. I'd explain to anyone who was interested exactly what happened when he did a specific exercise for a certain body part; how incline presses stressed upper pecs, how concentration curls added "peak" to biceps, how chin-ups thickened a back. Soon I garnered a reputation as a person who was very knowledgeable in the field of bodybuilding—if nothing else.

Despite seeing the transformation that had come over their son, my mother and father decided to come down on my new pastime. "Louie, you'll never earn a living by building muscles," my mother used to tell me, while my dad would make gestures that suggested I was sick in the head for even attempting it. One day, after many months of training, I finally got to the point where I could strict curl a 100-pound barbell for six reps. This, to me, was a considerable accomplishment. Wanting to show my dad that all of my training did serve a purpose (i.e., it

made me stronger, which even he could not disapprove of), I called him downstairs to watch me.

"Hey, Dad, watch this!" I exclaimed proudly as I took a firm grip on the barbell and slowly stood upright, resting the bar across the front of my thighs. I then began to curl that monster, not six times but eight times! When I finally put it down, my biceps felt as though somebody had just taken a blowtorch to them. I was proud of myself, and I'm sure my expression suggested as much to my father.

A strange look came over his face. "Wow, that's pretty impressive, Louie," he said, which made me feel great. "Let me see how heavy that barbell really is." He walked over to the barbell and took a grip, picked it up off the floor, and held it on the front of his thighs as I had done. For him to have said the word "impressive" meant a lot to me, as he'd never said it before. I felt good. My father then slowly attempted to curl the weight; he moved it up one inch and, struggling, lifted it an inch more. "Aaaagh," he grunted, "boy, that is heavy, Louie!" I nodded, the smile widening on my face. "See, Dad, even

though I have my problems, my weight training has at least made me a stronger person," I said with pride.

"Sure, Louie," my dad said, and then, with a huge laugh, he proceeded to curl that 100-pound barbell 17 times in succession! He had been playing possum! I can still hear his laughter as he then dropped it down onto the floor and the sarcastic tone in his voice as he added, "Yeah, that weightlifting has really paid off for you." Then he left the room.

I burned. I had always hated being tricked, and being tricked by a parent is particularly hurtful, as it takes away any sort of solace or recourse that most parents can offer their children if they're ever duped by an outsider. Once again, I would have to rely on myself alone to recover from this shot.

I vowed right there and then that I would get stronger, so strong in fact that on his best day, my father would never be able to best me in any strength event I decided to perform. I would show him—and anybody else who doubted it—just how powerful and productive bodybuilding could be.

3
The Role of Heroes

Like most other young boys, I placed a lot of stock in having heroes and role models. They were paradigms of success to look up to and admire. Heroes set standards of performance and conduct that could motivate and inspire me to improve myself. In looking back on my developmental years, I believe the main reason for my continued search for an adequate role model was the complete paucity of them in my immediate surroundings. As is often the case, existing social conditions served to mold certain facets of my personality. I was quiet and not prone to express my opinions because I was taught that my observations and experiences meant little to my parents. As a result, I withdrew and wished to be like someone else, someone perfect, with no physical or character defects. "What a feeling that must be," I fantasized at the time, "to be looked up to and respected."

I fantasized a lot more than most people of my age, and my fantasy world became very real to me for a time. It was a form of escape from the pathetic folly that my role in the real world had become. It was a world of exploration wherein I

Steve Reeves

could put myself in the shoes of a successful and respected individual and try to comprehend what his life must be like—and how my own would be—how I would be treated if I were this person, and how I would treat others.

I would daydream all day long, and my daydreams and fantasies would never have an ending. I remember hating the sound of my alarm clock—but not for the reasons that most people do. To others, the alarm represents an unwelcome call to leave the comfort of bed and head out to work. To me, it represented the intrusion of a cold and often cruel existence that had ended my creative and fascinating world of wonder. I was always disappointed when I woke up and realized that my dream was over—or at least temporarily preempted. It's a condition in which I still indulge today, although I've learned how to make my dreams parallel (to a certain extent) the reality of the world in a harmonious way.

As I mentioned in Chapter 2, my first "real" hero (other than my father) was Steve Reeves. To me, Reeves had it all. From the moment that Brooklyn evening when Hercules came flickering across our television screen, Reeves had become my role model. I wanted to be like Steve Reeves more than I wanted anything else in the

Steve Reeves

world. He was tall, had a terrific build, possessed incredible strength, was exceptionally good looking, and appeared quite capable of taking care of himself. He had a rugged, outdoorsy look that I found very impressive. I think Reeves's impact was so great because I, in many respects, was his polar opposite; I possessed none of those qualities that he had in such abundance. I was skinny, not that good looking, unattractive to girls, and getting beaten up all the time and unable to defend myself. Reeves reinforced my belief of what could be achieved with the human body through proper training and dedication.

The image of Reeves's physique fanned the flames of my ambition, and I started training harder than ever before, hoping to build myself up as Reeves himself had many years previously. Having such low self-esteem, I wanted to build up right away so that all of my problems, or a major portion of them, would be solved. Whenever I felt like skipping a workout, I'd make myself remember the way Reeves looked on film, the way his muscles moved and twitched whenever he'd lift some heavy object or pull something toward him. The image reinforced my resolve to improve and grow stronger. I became fascinated with muscle tissue and its structure and function.

During this period of my teenage years, Reeves embodied everything I hoped to aspire to; he was strong, muscular, and handsome, a movie star who was worshipped by millions of fans and wealthy to boot. What more was there to life? This guy had it all—in spades! Plus, that scene at the end of the Hercules movie where he pulled down the pillars with his bare hands— Man!—it just blew me away.

Exit Hercules, Enter the Blond Adonis

As a rule, my heroes were tall men like me. At 6'1", Reeves naturally appealed to me, and years later Arnold Schwarzenegger would inspire me for similar reasons, as would Dave Draper, a blond six-footer with incredible arms. However, I once made an exception to this height rule; it came after my second year of training. The reason for my break with tradition can be summarized in two words: Larry Scott.

Larry Scott was only 5'8", but he hit the bodybuilding world of the mid-1960s with the impact of a cruise missile. I loved Reeves's physique, but his era was the 1940s, and he wasn't a cover attraction in the muscle magazines anymore, whereas Larry Scott, the reigning champion, was featured liberally—and with good reason. Scott had a phenomenal physique; his shoulders and arms alone startled me. Even

Dave Draper

the way he appeared in the fuzzy black-and-white photos wiped me out. I was so impressed that I used to cut his pictures out and stare at them for hours. I wanted so badly to be built like Larry Scott. He was called the "Blond Adonis" of bodybuilding because he epitomized the California bodybuilding culture of the 1960s. He had blond hair and a golden-brown tan and was always photographed outside in the California sunshine, usually wearing a muscle shirt (tank top) and sunglasses. It was such a cool look that I was instantly riveted.

In many ways, I preferred his look to that of Reeves. Scott had such incredible arms, particularly his biceps which looked to me to be the size of basketballs. There's a famous shot of Scott standing outside of Vince Gironda's North Hollywood gym with Freddie Ortiz. The two of them are flexing their awesome arms (Ortiz was Scott's main rival for "Best Arms" in bodybuilding back in those days) as the sun beats down on them. When I'd be walking home from school in the dead of winter in Brooklyn, that image fired me up to train and kept me warm. It also (although I wouldn't realize this until much later) planted the first seeds of moving to California to train year-round in the fresh air and sunshine. What a lifestyle that must be, I thought to myself as I hurried downstairs to my home gym and trained my biceps using Larry's famous "tri-set" routine (doing three different exercises in a row without resting).

In time, as my body gradually started to respond to my training, I learned that Larry Scott and I had similarly shaped arms, genetically speaking, and that he, like me, had started with very poor genetics overall. I was heartened by the fact that, despite the handicap of narrow shoulders and low natural potential, Scott was able to build the greatest physique of his day, and he did it simply through hard and diligent training. He was able to maximize his potential

Larry Scott

through perseverance and outright hard work. This proved that there was still hope for me to do likewise. Knowing that he had to overcome such disadvantages increased my admiration for him.

When I learned that Scott would be competing in the second Mr. Olympia contest (he had already won the first) in New York, I took the news the same way a good Catholic would when informed that the Pope was coming to town: I had to go and see him. Not meet him, necessarily, but see him!

It was 1966, and I was in my first year of high school at Brooklyn Tech. To my surprise and delight, I learned that the Mr. Olympia contest that year was to be held right across the street from my school at the Brooklyn Academy of Music. I saved my money for months and bought a ticket as soon as they became available. I sat in the first row of the balcony and waited for the man whom I'd known only from pictures in a magazine to come to life before my eyes.

Although I knew Scott would be impressive, I had no idea of what was to come. When Larry finally appeared onstage, the audience went dead silent. They were stunned by the huge delts, the swollen biceps, the sweeping lats, and the flaring quadriceps that rippled as he strode across the stage. It was like watching a beautiful wild animal in its natural habitat. And when he hit his first double-biceps pose, the audience went nuts! I've never, to this day, seen anybody get an ovation like the one Larry Scott received from that crowd in Brooklyn that night—and I'm including Arnold at his absolute best when I say this.

Seeing Larry Scott at that point of my life was the nearest thing to a religious experience that I'd ever had; I'd honestly thought that I'd just seen God. I was mesmerized. I remember looking down from the balcony and seeing Larry at the corner of the stage pumping up those incredible biceps and how awesome they looked: thick, round, and full. And how the people cheered for him that night! I decided as I sat in that darkened auditorium that this was what I wanted for myself. I would build my body up as Larry Scott had and take to the stage and be as admired and worshipped as he was that night in Brooklyn! This is not to say that he necessarily had the best physique in the world at that time, as there also existed a colossus from Cuba by the name of Sergio Oliva, who not only was competing against Scott that evening but also was far and away more muscular, with more complete development. However, Larry Scott was so popular that night that, if he had lost, there would surely have been a riot.

After the contest, I hurried home to reexamine all of my Larry Scott training articles. I also read about his personal life and was impressed by the fact that he was married to a nice Japanese woman, was a devout Mormon, and conducted himself like a gentleman at all times (I'm pleased to note that he still does to this day). At that moment, as I reread my magazines with a flashlight under my covers, Larry Scott became the living, breathing embodiment of the all-American hero.

Reaching a Higher Level

After a few more years, and as I got taller, I found that some of the exercises that worked for Larry didn't work for me or caused considerable discomfort. He would do dips, for example, in a fashion that did nothing but cause severe pain in my shoulder joints. This bothered me, since I knew that I had to train like Scott if I ever hoped to acquire a physique like his.

It so happened that at this period of the '60s, a new bodybuilder was starting to emerge on the competitive scene—one who would soon revolutionize the sport and carry it into the 1970s. To my delight, this bodybuilder was over six feet tall. His name was Arnold Schwarzenegger.

I'd found a new hero in Arnold, and he would remain so up until the moment I decided to compete against him in 1974. While Larry had great arms and shoulders, Arnold had more complete body development. And, with a 21-inch

arm, he'd elevated bodybuilding to a new level entirely.

I saw Arnold in person for the first time when I was 17 years old. Through his police connections my dad got special permission for us to enter the backstage area of the 1969 Mr. Olympia IFBB competition at the Brooklyn Academy of Music. I couldn't wait to see this guy in the flesh after having read about him for a full year. When he first came on the scene, I saw a picture of him in a "praying mantis" pose. I'd never seen anybody with biceps so thick! I said to myself, "My God! This guy's like a monster!" The comic book store I used to frequent carried a small powerlifting magazine that was imported from England. The publisher was a gentleman I would later come to know quite well by the name of Oscar Heidenstam. One issue had shots of Arnold at Chet Yorton's Universe contest. I couldn't believe the thickness of Arnold's back! It was way ahead of the level of development of any champion in the United States at the time.

Arnold was walking around backstage when I first caught a glimpse of him. He was wearing cutoff sweatpants and a cutoff sweatshirt while he was pumping up, preparing to go onstage. I had big black-rimmed glasses, and my eyes were riveted to him as he went through his pre-posing preparations. It was the thrill of my life. After Arnold appeared to be finished pumping up, my father approached him. "Would you give my son an autograph?" he asked. Arnold replied in a harsh tone, "Not now! Later on!" I was devastated, but I realize today that he was so into the contest that he meant the refusal in a different way from how I interpreted it. In fact, when people ask me for autographs, I usually don't like to sign them when I'm pumping up either. I know that sometimes it's hard for the public to understand what a bodybuilder goes through. The fact is that interrupting a bodybuilder pumping up for a contest is the equivalent of walking up to a baseball player who's in the on-deck circle during the middle of a major-league baseball game and asking him to sign a ball. There's a time and a place for everything, if you get my drift.

Still, when Arnold took his sweats off and walked out onstage, I just shook my head in disbelief. "This is it," I said to myself. "This is the ultimate bodybuilder. This is the person I want to be like." And then a new thought came into my mind almost instantly. "No, Louie," I said, "you're going to be bigger than this guy! You're going to be stronger than this guy—and you're going to be more muscular than this guy! He's simply opened the door for you to walk through." This was a pretty wild and revolutionary thought for an introvert. However, it alerted me to the fact that, somewhere within the recesses of my psyche, I thought I had potential—that I was important and capable of not only competing with but ultimately defeating the greatest bodybuilder in the world. Arnold did not intimidate me in the least.

When Arnold walked down the street after the contest, hundreds of people followed him. It was an incredible, awe-inspiring sight. Then my bold thoughts returned. "Someday, Louie, they'll be doing that for you!" I told myself. A strange feeling surged through me, a warm rush of confidence and hope for my future. It was a good feeling—an enjoyable feeling—the best that I'd felt about myself in a long, long time.

As I entered our family home, I felt so good I wanted to share my experience and newfound belief in myself with somebody. Anybody. As it happened, my father, who had left the contest before me, was sitting in the living room. "Dad," I said, with a certain amount of pride in my voice, "someday I'm going to be bigger than Arnold—I'm going to beat him! I really believe I can do it, Dad." My father looked up from his paper, and his eyes met mine. "No, you won't," he said firmly. "Arnold has his hearing. You don't have normal hearing like Arnold. You'll never do it." Then he lowered his eyes to his paper and continued reading.

Arnold Schwarzenegger

4
Overcoming Adversity

My father's lack of encouragement was something I'd learned to take in stride. To him, I was always an embarrassment, a screw-up, the one who would always fumble the ball and who lacked both the intellect and natural talent to ever succeed in anything. Certainly my future was going to be far paler than his own.

What strikes me as amazing now is that I was able to succeed at all in such a repressive atmosphere. I was being rejected and ignored by my father during this time in my life. If I showed success in something, such as receiving a good grade or turning in a solid athletic performance, he was happy (though never complimentary) and willing to hold off on the sarcasm and the abuse. If I was unsuccessful, however, such as if I failed to win a contest, then he didn't want to know me. It was as if my falling short were a deliberate affront to him.

As an example, in the movie *Pumping Iron*, I was featured as one of the top challengers to end Arnold's reign as Mr. Olympia. George Butler and the crew of White Mountain Films had decided to film a documentary about bodybuilders and the top contest in the sport, so they had followed us to South Africa to capture the 1975 Mr. Olympia contest. Despite the suggestion made by the film, the '75 Mr. Olympia contest was one bodybuilding competition I never wanted to enter. Many people within the sport seem to be of the impression that Arnold won that contest because he "psyched" me out moments before we stepped onstage to compete in the finals. Well, folks, the truth is that this boy was defeated long before he'd even stepped on the plane. Besides, as bodybuilding contests are decided for the most part at the prejudging, anything Arnold may have done by the time of the finals would have been, in effect, too little, too late.

Still, almost from the day I had agreed to compete in that contest, I wished that I hadn't. I knew that I just wasn't as focused on the event as I needed to be to win. My home life had deteriorated so badly and my relationship with my father had become so awful that, mentally, I was unprepared to do battle for the greatest title in professional bodybuilding.

I wouldn't have competed at all but for the fact that, for the time being, I still had to live at home, and Dad viewed both the contest and particularly the film as tremendous publicity vehicles for himself. He saw *Pumping Iron* as his opportunity to be a "movie star" and saw me as his vehicle to accomplishing this. We were shown training together in the film, whereas in real life we never trained together at all. He was depicted in the film as being compassionate and caring about my career, whereas in real life he never gave it a second's thought. The producers thought it would add a nice, warm "family" angle to the picture (had they only known!) if my dad was involved in almost every facet of contest preparation—and he was only too happy to oblige. After we had completed our work before the cameras in *Pumping Iron*, I asked my dad if he wanted to go to the gym with me for a workout. His eyes widened in disbelief. "What, are you nuts?" he replied. "I never want to go to the gym with you again!"

Once I arrived in South Africa to compete, the feeling of despair grew. Whenever I would pass Arnold in the lobby of the hotel where we were staying in preparation for the competition, my impulse was to take him aside and say, "Hey, let's go on a fishing boat. Let's get out of here and take a vacation. Let's just get out of here! Screw the damn contest!" I truly wanted to run away. I was so unhappy, so miserable, that I just wanted to get away from the whole environment of deception that was being played out on a daily basis before the cameras. I knew that my mental attitude was a thousand miles from where it needed to be if I was really going to take a serious shot at winning the contest.

Although I suspected I was going to lose before the contest even began, after the prejudging had ended, I was positive. I knew that it was all over. For that matter, as I said, I knew I'd lost before I ever set foot in South Africa. Still, Arnold leaned over to me during the prejudging and said, "Don't worry about it, Louie, we'll have some fun tonight when we pose." I thought to myself, "Great. Even though the final placings haven't been officially announced, it's already obvious that I'm not in the kind of shape I need to be in to even make a contest out of this."

It was with heavy steps that I went back to the hotel and walked into our room. There, lying on the bed, watching TV was my father—this man whom George Butler was painting as being a warm, caring man who only wanted to see his boy do well. That man was fantasy Dad; he didn't exist. In his place was real Dad, who was now filled with rage at the fact that his son was going to lose the contest when it came time for the finals later that night—and make him look stupid once more for having brought such a loser into the world. He stood up and said calmly and coldly, "Listen, when we go home, I want you to go out and get a real job—I want you out of my house!" Once again, he'd seized the opportunity to kick me when I was down and most vulnerable. At 23 years of age, I began to sob uncontrollably. My mother came in and tried to console me but it was no use. I felt as though my life were doomed, and I cried like a baby.

My self-esteem was so low that I felt completely unworthy—not so much as a competitor but as a human being. I honestly did not believe that I was worthy enough as a person to even step onstage to compete against people who were (for want of a better term) "normal." To better explain this dejection, it's necessary for me to go back to 1973 and what was, ironically, one of the proudest moments of my young competitive life: winning the IFBB Mr. Universe title.

Mr. Universe

Winning the Mr. Universe contest was the pinnacle of my golden dream. Arnold had won the contest, as well as Larry Scott before him. My win proved to me that I didn't need to be blessed with perfect hearing to be successful. Taking that title was, to me at least, no small accomplishment, as it reaffirmed my belief in myself and justified all those nights in my basement working out, pushing myself to the limit, enduring the incredible pain that only seasoned iron pumpers and top-level athletes can relate to. It also proved, in a sense, that my perception of things was alright, that Lou Ferrigno's brain was fully capable of discerning what was possible or impossible and determining the best way to achieve the possible. Despite all the negative reinforcement I received at home such as "You'll never do it," "What do you hope to accomplish spending all that time in the gym?" and the ever-present "They're never going to give the Universe title to a deaf person," I knew that if I just focused my sights and held fast, I could do it. And, if I could win the Universe, or so I thought in my heart of hearts, then maybe—just maybe—I could become a successful professional bodybuilder just like my heroes Reeves, Scott, and Schwarzenegger.

After I won the Mr. Universe title, I was on top of the world. I felt, honestly and truly, proud of myself. "Yes!" I thought, "I've done it!" I also knew that the ABC television network had promised to broadcast the contest several weeks later on their *Wide World of Sports* program, which meant national exposure. I would be "known!" You can't imagine how good that felt; not only did I win the highest amateur title in bodybuilding, but an ABC commentator sought me out and interviewed me immediately afterward. I would have the opportunity of sharing the proudest day of my life with all of my friends and family, and the rest of the country as well! I was over the moon!

Dad told me that he was going to go down to the ABC studios in New York City to take an advance look at the contest tape they were intending to broadcast. I didn't think much about it when he said it, but I felt a little bit of pride that he was starting to express an interest in something in which I was successful. In any event, the day Dad went to the studio was the longest one I've ever experienced. All sorts of thoughts went through my head: Would I look as impressive on the tape as I'd looked on the stage? How did I comport myself for the interview? Did I convey just how wonderful the sport of bodybuilding truly was for me? I knew that when Dad came home, he would be able to answer all of my questions for me and give me a preview of what all of America would soon be seeing on their television sets on a forthcoming Saturday afternoon.

What happened that day had an impact that has lasted the rest of my life. Sitting in the back-seat of the family car, waiting for my father's train to arrive, I could barely contain my excitement. Suddenly I caught a glimpse of Dad coming up the stairs from the station, but instead of a proud, broad smile, he had a cold, hard look on his face. I looked at my mother in worried anticipation and grabbed hold of the handrail on the car door. "What happened?" I thought to myself. "Maybe the show's been canceled." The door to the car suddenly opened, and Dad plopped himself down in the front seat. He didn't say a word. Having waited on pins and needles since his departure earlier that morning, I was anxious to hear his report as the first member of the general public to have seen footage of the contest. My main concern was "Did I really look as if I deserved the win?" Although I firmly believed it, I needed that vote of confidence. After all, millions of people, or so I hoped, would be watching the tape soon, and I wanted to come across as a worthy champion.

After almost 30 seconds I decided I should initiate the conversation. "Hey, how was the show and everything?" I asked. He looked at me coldly and said, "You know something? They can't use your interview because we can't understand your speech! Your speech was awful!" Caught unaware by his attack, I was defenseless for his final shot, "You're a misfit!"

Nothing I had had to endure up until that point could equal the devastation of his three-sentence salvo. I was shocked, horrified, hurt, and stunned into total silence. I'd gone from a world champion with a bright future only moments before to the lowest piece of trash on the planet. I tried to defend myself. "What do you want from me?" I protested as I prepared to play what I was sure would be my trump card. "I won the Mr. Universe contest!" His eyes grew even colder at my remark. "It was wasted on you!" he hissed, and then added, "It should have been me!"

A sense of frustration once again crept back into my world. I knew I just could not satisfy this man. I gave up then and there, thinking to myself, "It just doesn't matter anymore. It doesn't mean anything that I was chosen as one of the greatest bodybuilders in the world. It doesn't matter that I won one of the sport's most prestigious titles. It doesn't matter that it was being covered by a major network, that my victory would be shown on TV. It doesn't matter that I was going to receive more publicity and exposure through that victory than any other bodybuilder had (as even Arnold had yet to get any television exposure at that point in his bodybuilding career)"—none of it mattered. This person who was sitting in front of me—and who was a family member to boot—was once again putting me down because of a handicap that I can't do anything about. I wanted to crawl away and die.

The tape of the contest did air later on, without my interview of course, and also without a shot of me actually winning the contest. They showed me and several other competitors hitting poses, and then they cut away to another sport. Howard Cosell did a voiceover saying, "By the way, ladies and gentlemen, Lou Ferrigno won the Mr. Universe contest. And now back to championship boxing featuring Muhammad Ali and Ken Norton." I perceived this to be another strike at me. My proudest moment had been reduced to network filler, a footnote in somebody else's book.

Still, it was my dad's comments that cut the deepest. My father calling me a misfit had such an effect that, for the moment, I gave up all hope of ever competing again. I just knew that I didn't have the personality or the eloquence to successfully promote myself. No matter how hard I trained, how much I sacrificed, or how many titles I won, it ultimately didn't matter a damn because people would always think of me as a big deaf guy with no future. I had entered a condition that some psychologists characterize as "learned helplessness." That's why when I eventually did go to South Africa to compete against Arnold, I was so impressed by the way he could sway a crowd. He had people following him everywhere, idolizing him and hanging on his every word. This aspect about Arnold impressed

me far more than his physique. He'd shown me nothing, musclewise, that gave me cause for concern, but his personality, charisma, and incredible self-confidence were wonders to behold because I was completely lacking in these departments.

Opportunity Knocks

A bright light shone through the darkened tunnel of my life briefly the next month. Joe Weider, the multimillionaire bodybuilding publisher and the man who had discovered or trained every major physique star in bodybuilding since the 1940s, called our house in Brooklyn. He had moved from Newark to California and was interested in having me move out to California to pursue my bodybuilding career. "The kid's got the greatest potential I've ever seen!" he'd exclaimed. Unfortunately, my dad thought otherwise. "No, he's not interested, Mr. Weider," he replied, and hung up the phone. He hung up on Joe Weider!—the one man who honestly thought I had a future and was in a position to do something about it. Now he'd been told to "get lost." It wasn't likely that opportunity was going to knock a second time at Lou Ferrigno's door. The bright light of hope had been extinguished almost as soon as it had appeared.

The reason my dad was so adamant about my not going to California (although I didn't realize it at the time) was that my doing so would have represented two things: I would have been outside the realm of his control, and he would have lost a source of income. You have to understand that by the time I was capable of working—that is, of bringing home money—a new rule was passed in the Ferrigno household: "All money goes to Dad." My father had incurred some heavy losses in the stock market and decided that it was best to make his children his indentured servants to earn money to pay back the debt. As a result, for a good number of years, I never had any disposable income. Dad viewed me as sort of his own personal ploughhorse; as long as he was steering me in the right direction and holding the reins, all of my labors could be directed in such a way as to benefit him.

I learned this lesson when I was 12 years old and had just finished a nine-hour shift delivering groceries to customers of a local supermarket; for this laborious task, I was awarded the princely sum of 25 cents per delivery. By the end of the day, I had made $9.35 after deductions. I came home and put all my money out on the kitchen table. There it was, the collective fruits of nine hours of labor. My father was eating at the table and slowly looked up from his food. "How much you make, Louie?" he asked. "It's $9.35!" I said excitedly. "I'm going to go buy something!" He just shook his head. "No, you're not. Hand the money over to your mother," he replied. My mother nodded in agreement. "No, we're going to look after it," she added.

For a moment, I forgot who I was talking to and lost my temper. "But I earned this money! I could have gone out to the park and played ball or anything—but I chose to work this morning so I could buy something!" Dad was unmoved. I looked at him sitting there in his undershirt eating his food, and the unfairness of it all became immediately obvious, particularly since all of my friends in the neighborhood had their own money to go to shows or buy new clothes with. "I worked hard for that money, Dad," I protested. "What did you earn this morning?" My father's face went white with rage. He took hold of a butcher knife and threw it at me with all of his might! I was fortunate that my reflexes were such that I was able to duck out of its path. The knife whistled past my nose. "You've got some nerve saying that to me!" he shrieked at the top of his lungs. I was terrified that my own father would try to kill me over a quarrel regarding such a pitiful amount of money. I couldn't understand why he was behaving this way, but, needless to say, I left the money on the table.

This went on until I was well over 21 and was working part time at a funeral home as a pallbearer for a grand total of $30 per weekend. He refused to let me live by myself or to have my own car; every

penny had to go to him. This was pure control. As a result, I had no motivation to work harder at any vocation—except bodybuilding. He could never take that away from me. Any accolades or rewards that I received in this arena weren't of sufficient value to my father to try to take.

My golden opportunity to escape presented itself in 1976, when I was invited to California to guest pose. One of the co-owners of Gold's Gym in Venice had told me that I'd made an impression upon the bodybuilding public through my appearances in the bodybuilding magazines and at the 1975 Mr. Olympia contest. He wanted me to guest pose at one of his West Coast contests. Because it was considered a "quick score" (I would receive $200 for my exhibition), I encountered no resistance from my father.

As soon as the plane touched down in California, I knew that this was where I wanted to be. This was where I belonged. Here there were opportunities for me to be successful in the one thing I cared about—bodybuilding. It didn't matter that I didn't know a soul. It didn't even matter that I was broke and had to sleep on the beach for two weeks—none of it mattered because this was going to be my new home.

I found out from some of the local bodybuilders where Joe Weider's office was and, after having fulfilled my guest-posing duties, traveled up to Woodland Hills to meet with him and tell him my story. "Look," I said, "I want to stay in California to train for your Mr. Olympia contest. I know that you gave Arnold a contract when he first came out here; could you please do likewise for me? I'll clean toilets at your office—anything—just give me a source of income out here." Joe knew I was sincere and, being a bodybuilder at heart, empathized with my plight. To make a long story short, he gave me a contract. I got a car and an apartment, and I never went home again.

Still, that didn't mean that, when I eventually did break away from my father's control and started to become successful, he stopped trying to excise his pound of flesh. He was furious that I'd decided to stay in California, and he tried

every form of personal attack and vilification that he could think of to get his top ploughhorse back. "You've let the family down!" he said in one call. "We're all ashamed of you." I knew, deep down, that his words did not represent the view of all the members of my family, but rather only his own. His next tactic was to ask me to send him money with the intention that he would "look after it" and I would live "within my means." All the time he was trying to discourage me from living in California, since he couldn't exert any influence or control over me from so far away.

It was a sad time for me personally, as he did all that he could to turn the rest of my family against me in a further effort to lay his guilt trip on me. However, I soon recognized that he would show some concern for my well-being (I thought it was love at the time) only when I was winning or earning money for him.

Once Joe Weider increased my exposure in his magazines and played up the significance of my Mr. Universe win, my father realized that his ploughhorse was fast becoming a golden goose. I was now capable of making even more money and establishing far greater business contacts than would have ever been possible had I opted to remain in Brooklyn.

Not wanting to miss out on the action, he approached me about starting a business to be called "The Lou Ferrigno Sports Center," the purpose of which was to provide an income for my brother and family. When I subsequently learned that it was simply another project to give my dad pocket money and that I wouldn't receive a penny or any direct benefit, I became enraged. Here was a man who did nothing but run me down, telling me that a deaf person was next to useless and that I, personally, was a complete misfit. Now he was trying to slip yet another harness around my shoulders from 3,000 miles away and take advantage of me. From somewhere I summoned the courage and told him to change the name, to take my name off of anything he was promoting, because I wanted nothing at all to do with it. If he wanted to make money, I reasoned, then he could do it as I did— on his own.

5
My Formula for Success

Through amateur self-analysis I've concluded that four key components are responsible for my life's turning around and changing from absolutely awful to successful. They are:

- Self-Belief
- Consistency
- Determination
- Persistence

These are the four "big ones"—the factors without which your life may be doomed to stagnation but that can make all your hopes and dreams come true (or at least enter the realm of possibility) if you rely on their importance. They will either make or break your chances for success. Let's look at each component in closer detail.

Self-Belief

Self-belief is an aftereffect of looking back on a series of short-term goals that you have already achieved. In this respect, it is a form of applied retrospection, using your past to inspire your future.

In order to develop this belief in yourself, you first have to choose as a challenge something—anything—that you enjoy doing. Then you must be confident that your goal is obtainable. Once you've placed a mental check mark beside these two boxes, all that remains is to go for it—and go for it with 100 percent of your abilities and energy!

This is not to present a too-simplistic logic to acquiring self-belief. Granted, you're going to encounter a lot of obstacles along the way, depending on the outcome you choose to reach, but you can't let anything deter you from the attainment of your short-term (and eventually long-term) goals. You've just got to keep telling yourself, "Yes, there are going to be hard days en route to attaining this goal—but there are going to be good days and easy days as well. Despite the bad times, I'm just going to keep on doing it." Once you've selected a definite goal to strive for, and you believe that you can obtain it, there's no reason for you to miss.

Consistency

"Rome wasn't built in a day," and neither was anything else of significant value. In bodybuilding, reaching the upper limits of your genetic potential can take years. Many bodybuilders with tremendous potential often give up part of the way through the journey because they lacked one thing in their training—consistency.

In bodybuilding, if your goal is to be the best in the world, it's mandatory that you make your training your number-one priority. Training must be more important than anything else in your life. You must make space in your daily living schedule to include your exercise sessions—and never miss a session. Whether your goal is to become Mr. Olympia or simply to firm up and drop a few pounds, goals are obtainable only when you give yourself over to their pursuit 100 percent. Granted, if you're legitimately sick or have the flu, then it will definitely benefit you to give your body some extra rest by forgoing training for that day, but don't miss a workout for any other reason. Don't miss your designated training sessions, stick with your diet, and obtain adequate rest. These are the three "magic" ingredients for bodybuilding success. If you maintain the particulars but change the specifics, this same policy can be applied to anything else in life. The key is consistency. If you are as consistent as you possibly can be, 365 days a year, you can't miss.

Determination

The third component of success is determination, which I define as the will to succeed and drive forward. It's something that truly comes from within. You've got to locate it within you and cultivate your passion for the pursuit of your goal.

People can't give it to you; you can't run around and talk to 20 different psychologists and say, "Listen, I need you to give me some determination!" It doesn't happen that way. People can give you advice—and that's all. Any progress or success you experience has to come from your own efforts, not those of other people. Nobody can live your life for you, nor experience the pains and joys that come from it for you. Only you can do it.

You have to be the one who takes the chances and reaps the laurels for having done so. That's what makes life's victories so sweet. The greater the adversity you must overcome to obtain your goal, the greater your enjoyment and resulting increase in self-esteem. Don't dwell on the potential that exists to trip up; after all, we all make mistakes, and we are all going to fail in some way or another as we travel along life's path. If you're willing to carry on in spite of the odd setback, then such setbacks will always be minor.

Think about it this way: When you first learned how to walk, you tripped and fell constantly, but you got back up again and carried on. When children are born, they're free of the misconceptions and worries that adults possess, so they can conceive of all things as being possible. If children fall, they get up! They fall again and they get up again. Eventually, however, determination pays off, and they learn to walk.

The ogres of self-doubt and pessimism start to manifest in our psyches as we get older, when we become influenced by others who tell us, "You can't do this" or "You can't do that." If we had to learn to walk at an older age, after having been subjected to such negativity, the majority of us might still be crawling on the floor! We'd be thinking to ourselves, "Forget it! This is too hard to do! That guy was right." But as a child, you don't know about any of that. You don't put any stock in other people's opinions. You simply have the determination to walk—and, with nothing else, you eventually learn. It's a simple process, and it's exactly the same with anything else in life. Sure, you might trip, but you know you're going to get up again. As long as you are determined that you will reach your goal eventually, you've got it made.

Persistence

Again, the odd fall is going to beset even the most successful of us from time to time, but learning to deal with adversity, providing it isn't completely overwhelming, only serves to strengthen our resolve to be successful. This is what teaches you to become a champion. Persistence, the final component, is simply the will to succeed, the desire to keep going, and a refusal to quit. It all comes down to the passion of your conviction and the determination of knowing that you can do it. If you really want it, go for it. Trust your decisions, and then stand by them. People who become world leaders and champions in their chosen vocations believe in their abilities and continue to hold fast to their dreams until they attain them.

The Role of Short-Term Goals

One of the best techniques I've used to facilitate success is to break down my goals into the categories of immediate (short term) or long term. If you set a long-term goal but haven't set any short-term goals, you can find yourself discouraged, because long-term goals aren't reached overnight. You must view goal attainment as a journey, and it's a long road ahead of you.

I'm talking about a duration of 5 to 10 years for the attainment of a long-term goal. Short-term goals allow you to assess the progress you've made and the distance you've already traveled—a further confidence-booster for reaching your long-term destination.

Toward this end, you should also keep a diary. If your goal centers on bodybuilding, you can use a tape measure to determine your gains and then note your physical increases each month. Check your logbook regularly to see how strong you're getting, and appraise yourself in the mirror to validate your progress. Take pictures as you go along. Once you see the strides you've made within six months to a year, you'll realize how much closer you are to attaining your long-term goal.

Be realistic in your goal selection. For example, you can't put a picture of me or some other bodybuilding champion on the wall and say,

"Okay, I want to look like that when I'm 40." It's not that simple. When I first looked at Arnold, I knew that I was going to someday be bigger than he was, but on the other hand, I was still a kid, and his level of development seemed light years away from mine at that point. But I knew I could continue to make progress, bit by bit, so that eventually I would reach my potential, which, I believed, was superior to Arnold's. Surpassing Arnold's measurements was my long-term goal, with every inch of progress I made up until that point serving as self-affirming, short-term goals. I refused to give up, and after about five years of dedicated training I eventually bettered all of Arnold's measurements.

You've also got to be consistent with your training. You can't slack off, then lie to yourself and say, "Well, I've given it five months and I'm not any closer to my long-term goal." You've got to be honest with yourself. Maybe you trained only six times in six weeks during this period. If so, this can't be considered serious, dedicated, focused, purposeful training. Once you lie to yourself, you'll also find it easier to lie to everybody else, which leads to further self-esteem problems.

Honest self-communication is the key. Deal with reality. The bottom line is that all of us have certain genetics and certain abilities that are unique. You have to maximize what you have—that's all anybody can do!

Setting the Plan in Motion

In life, success comes in direct proportion to how effectively you set your plan in motion. A plan not acted upon is stillborn. To have a real shot at achieving your dream, you have to actualize your concepts. Again, it's a matter of setting up and then attaining a series of short-term goals until you ultimately achieve your long-term objective.

We already are familiar with short-term goals leading to long-term goals in our daily lives, though we may not realize it. For many people, one of these ways is called education. Typically, you go to elementary school for eight years, then high school for four, and then it's your choice to go on to college. Let's say you attend college for four years and receive your degree. Well, what's happened here? You've just achieved the long-term goal of obtaining a college education. This is something that is almost inbred in Americans. If, on the other hand, you don't attempt to complete your education, it's considered your own fault, and society will often brand you as a "loser." How do you get a complete education? Consistency. You can't get eight years' worth of education in one year—you have to keep at it.

You can apply the same concept of smaller, short-term goals to anything you do. It's called taking steps, and remember that the longest journey is completed through a series of small paces. It doesn't happen at once. Well-educated individuals don't become well educated overnight. They take a series of small steps to ultimately arrive at their destination. It just takes time and experience.

Experience is a great educator in itself. No matter what your age, if you open yourself up to try new things, you're going to experience some wondrous things. You'll also experience some tragedies to be sure, but then, it's never been scratched in stone that "life is perfect." Life is simply what you make it. Your job is to not let your goal be affected by anything else.

Do what you choose to do because you feel good about it and are happy with it. Don't let other people's opinions or negativity dissuade you. If you're not happy with your job, find something else that will make you happy. You have to find something in life that you enjoy doing and feel good engaging in. This, in turn, will help you to feel good about yourself and your occupation. Money isn't the sole criterion to be considered; you also must enjoy what you're doing.

This lesson applies with equal validity to bodybuilding. The longest journey begins with the first step, and you've just got to keep on walking. The more steps you take, the closer you will be to achieving your goal, whether it's losing some size off your hips, tightening your abdominals, or building a thicker chest and bigger arms. Again, the key here is to keep a realistic perspective. If you put up a picture of Arnold (who is 6'1") as your role model and you're only 5'8", that's not being realistic because you're never going to have the dimensions necessary to look like Arnold. Choose instead someone who's a better match to your height and bone structure.

Nevertheless, although you may never weigh 300 pounds in contest-ready shape, you can still possess the degree of muscularity that the champions do simply by making that your goal and by working diligently at it every day of your life. You can get the thickness, the depth, and the muscularity, if not the overall size, but what's wrong with that? Be the best that you can be—not a carbon copy of someone else.

Another key is to learn your strong suit and then follow through with it. For example, when I was younger, I had an active imagination that allowed my creative side to flourish, and in time, I entered the acting profession where such traits are considered a boon. In many respects, today's pop psychology books have missed the boat in their "can't see the forest for the trees" approach to creating personal happiness. If you desire to be happy and successful, the best advice is also the simplest: Find something that you enjoy doing. That's half the battle.

If you don't like your present job, stop for a moment and honestly think about what you enjoy doing. What are your hobbies? What do you find yourself thinking about when you are at work? These thoughts offer insights into your psyche, pointing to where your true interests lie. I'm not talking here about drugs or alcohol. That's just simple escapism. However, if you find you obtain personal rewards from books, from writing, from music—whatever your real interest—once you've determined the source of your enjoyment, stay with it.

When I was a child, a dream I held out was to be paid to train with weights. I always wished that I could make a living simply by working out. I wanted it so bad but was frequently discouraged in my pursuit. Yet, there was always a belief inside of me that someday I would be able to find such a job. And—you know something—it did happen! The result is that I now enjoy my life because I'm able to face every day knowing that I'll be able to do exactly the things that I enjoy doing. What's nice about bodybuilding and weight training is that they're wonderful tools to teach yourself about discipline. Let's say you like playing football—well, then, use bodybuilding as a tool to make yourself a stronger football player.

Perfecting Your Craft

Practice and Persistence

Certain attributes are essential to perfecting whatever craft or goal you happen to embrace. Number one, you have to commit yourself to engaging in whatever it is that is required for the successful performance of your craft. In my case, it was bodybuilding, and I never missed a workout, with the result that there wasn't an aspect of my physique that was neglected or underdeveloped. Make your practicing second nature by mere repetition; you want to have it as routine as possible. You need to go to bed at the same time, pack your gym bag or your clothes for the next day's workout well ahead of time, and write down your routine, sets, reps, and exercises. It may surprise you to learn, once you start keeping an up-to-date logbook, just how much progress you can make in a mere three months' time.

Two years ago, when I was preparing for my first contest after a 17-year layoff, I kept a diary to help track how much food I was consuming (because, after all, I would soon have to reduce that amount by a certain percentage in order to lose only body fat). I wrote down everything I ate and was shocked to discover how much food I was putting away on a daily basis. After count-

ing calories for three or four days (so that I would be assured that the calories I was consuming were indicative of my typical diet and not a subconscious effort to give myself a low reading), I cut out the food that I knew my body wasn't using or assimilating. Your mind can play tricks on you with regard to nutrition, so you should have your nutrition plan mapped out well ahead of time in your program. The plan serves as both a friendly reminder of what you hope to accomplish and a rearview mirror through which to see all of the short-term goals you have already achieved.

Self-Esteem

In addition to practice and persistence, self-esteem is vital, not just for bodybuilding or goal attainment, but for the healthy day-to-day functioning of our species in general. Self-esteem, as I define it, is simply the way you feel about yourself.

If you're always feeling bad about yourself, you have to discover the root cause of these feelings and then weed it out. Find out what bothers you the most, what affects your behavior and your outlook on life—and then do something about it. Remember that as human beings, we all have a mind, and in that mind resides the power of volition, or choice. Some people enjoy being miserable, and thus they find ways to bring misery on themselves. Again, it all comes down to volition.

We can choose either to continue to accept things the way they are or to change things, for better or worse. Never lose sight of the fact that you possess this power, just as every other human being does. The mind is stronger than the body, and we only have to be aware of this fact to realize that we have to take charge of our own lives. If you can do this, then you'll be in a position to finally take some action toward correcting your personal problems and forging your own unique future. Once this happens, I can guarantee that you will be a much happier person, and your self-confidence and self-esteem will skyrocket.

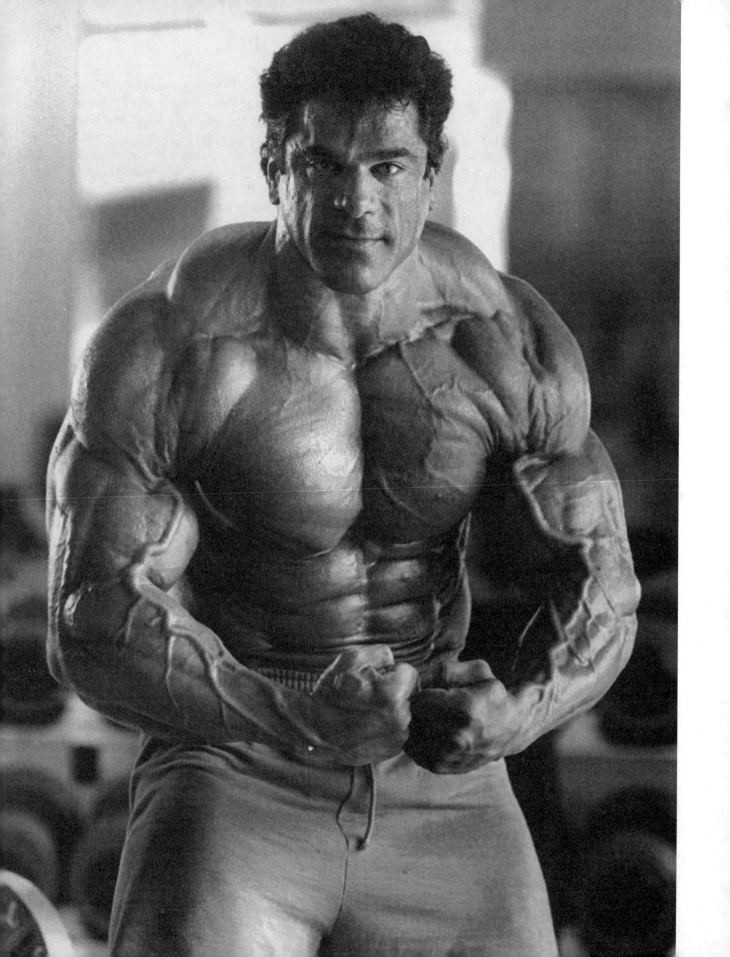

6
Life Begins at 40

In my younger days, I regarded 30 years of age as "over the hill." And I continued to feel this way right up until I turned 29. I even remember thinking at age 10 that age 20 was "old"! It's funny, in retrospect, how much aging is really just a state of mind. One man at 60 can be closer to the grave than another man at 80—depending on how he perceives himself and, more important, takes care of himself.

I recently got into my all-time best shape (or so I thought at the time) for the 1992 Mr. Olympia contest in Helsinki, Finland. It was quite an experience, and I feel I had to overcome almost as much adversity for this contest as I did during all my years of living with my father. I had been out of professional competitive bodybuilding for 17 years, having not set foot on a posing dais since the 1975 Mr. Olympia contest in which I placed third behind Arnold Schwarzenegger and Serge Nubret. As if that gap weren't cause enough for jitters, I was constantly being told, "Lou, you're too old. You're 40 years old, for God's sake. There's no way you can come back against these young kids."

This sentiment caught me by surprise. While I knew the new crop of Mr. Olympia competitors was very good indeed (men such as Sonny Schmidt, Lee Labrada, Paul Dillett, and—lest we forget—the incredible Englishman Dorian Yates),

I never once thought of myself as "over the hill." I'd kept in shape, and I assumed this was obvious to anyone who took the time to talk to me. Still, the naysayers persisted: "You're going to embarrass yourself, Lou!" "You don't belong up there onstage with all those young guys." All the words that had dogged me my whole life were being thrown in my face once again.

However, I'd developed some pretty thick scars from my first battering, and this time around I again refused to grant negative words any validity in their application to Lou Ferrigno. I just continued to train hard, watch my diet, and hope for the best.

Then my father called. "I won't be going to Helsinki to see you compete," he said. "Why's that, Dad?" I asked. "Because I can't handle seeing you lose again. You're too old." That's when I knew I had to come back—not just to try to win the title but, more important, to prove that at 40 years of age, a man can still get in great shape and be competitive against the best in the world!

Proving My Point

I trained from that point on with a demonlike intensity, working up to two two-hour workouts, six days a week, with another hour of aerobics thrown in. I don't think any other competitor in that contest displayed such dedication and determination. No, I didn't win the Mr. Olympia title that year; history will record that I placed what could be considered a distant twelfth over-all. But do you know what I saw in that contest? I saw a man who, at 40 years of age, soundly defeated men who were, in some instances, almost half his age. What history will also record—and it's a fact that makes me prouder than my placing—is that I got into my all-time best shape. I was ripped to the bone with cross-striations running throughout almost every muscle group in my body. I got the loudest ovation of any competitor that night, and that felt good because it confirmed that I'd established my point that evening. It also planted the competitive seed for the next Mr. Olympia the following year in Atlanta.

I knew that I could be even better in Atlanta than I had been in Finland. I knew that, at 41, I could be the first-ever bodybuilder to compete for the Mr. Olympia title at a body weight of more than 300 pounds of rock-solid, ripped-to-shreds muscle!

It would be a first—and it would take a 41-year-old man to do it.

I competed in Atlanta the following year at a competition-day body weight of 318 pounds! I even moved up a couple of placings, knocking off a few more young upstarts in the process. It felt good to go onstage for the second straight year after being away from the game so long and kick some serious butt!

Television crews followed my every move while I was in Atlanta, and this time, the comments were all different—by 180 degrees. "Oh, Lou, you looked incredible!" "You've never looked better!" And—I loved this one—"You're not really 40, are you?" The truth was that I really wasn't 40; I was closer to 42! But it was also true that I was in the best shape of my life.

More to the point, I felt good. I liked my body weight being up in the high 290s and even over 300 pounds. For years, Hollywood people

had told me, "You'll have to lose some size, or else you'll just dwarf everyone else." And for years, I fought to keep my weight down to the low 250s. However, this contest made me cognizant that being a small guy just isn't for me. I'm a bodybuilder, and I've trained hard, heavy, and with the expressed purpose of getting bigger, from the moment I first wrapped my fingers around a barbell. I've never gotten any pleasure from training to "get smaller!" I'm a big guy—I mean naturally big. I'm 6'5", and if I never worked out at all, I'd probably tip the scales at 275. For me to make a concerted effort to "lose size" didn't sit well.

This was all brought sharply into focus as soon as I got the green light to train for competition once more. It felt as if a huge burden had been lifted from my shoulders, and in a way, it had. If you remember anything from this book, it should be the core tenet of my formula for success: be true to yourself. Do those things that you want to do, not what other people think you should do.

For years, I did what all of those people in Hollywood wanted me to do and, for years before that, what my father wanted. I was successful in my earlier career only when I left home to actively pursue my own course, doing what I loved—bodybuilding. I was successful in Hollywood, for that matter, when I was the Hulk—as big as a house and doing what I wanted to do (i.e., training and getting big). I was successful, in other words, only when I was true to myself. Please don't infer from this, however, that the panacea to everyone's woes is simply to build big, massive muscles; that would be to miss my point entirely.

My happiness, or rather the one thing in life (apart from my wife and children) that brought me happiness and a sense of fulfillment, was bodybuilding. When I did that and put my heart and soul into it, nothing could stop me from being successful. For someone else, the venue might be painting, martial arts, driving a bus, or flying a plane. Whatever it is that makes you happy, vocationwise, do it! If you don't, you'll

end up miserable and filled with despair over what you should have done with your life.

I mention all of this because this is exactly how I felt when I decided, at 40 years of age, that I was going to "do it" again! I was going to be successful at the Mr. Olympia contest irrespective of where the judges would ultimately place me—because I was being true to myself. I was going to be engaged in a process of self-actualization, taking another step toward becoming the best that my potential would allow—and I did it!

Don't Let It Rust

Again, age is largely a mental condition anyway. People tend to "rust out" long before they "wear out," and I'm not the kind of person who opts for an inactive lifestyle. Neither is anyone else whose success is enduring. Look at Nolan Ryan, for example. That man kept going and going,

playing phenomenal baseball year after year. What about heavyweight boxer George Foreman? He came only a punch or two away from winning the heavyweight championship of the world—for the second time in his career, I might add—when he fought a much younger Evander Holyfield! Tell all of the opponents big George put to sleep during his comeback climb to the title that he's "too old." I think you might get a rather large argument.

And so it is with bodybuilding. How true it is that "what the mind can conceive, the body can achieve." Make your body the servant of your mind, and aspire to achieve great things in life. Aim for the stars and, at worst, you might hit the moon. But aim for the ceiling and you'll probably have to settle for the floor. Don't let anything stand in your way of achieving the body you want or the success you dream of. You can achieve both. All you've got to do is apply yourself to that which you truly love to do. Once you do that, you're already three-quarters of the way there—regardless of how "old" you are!

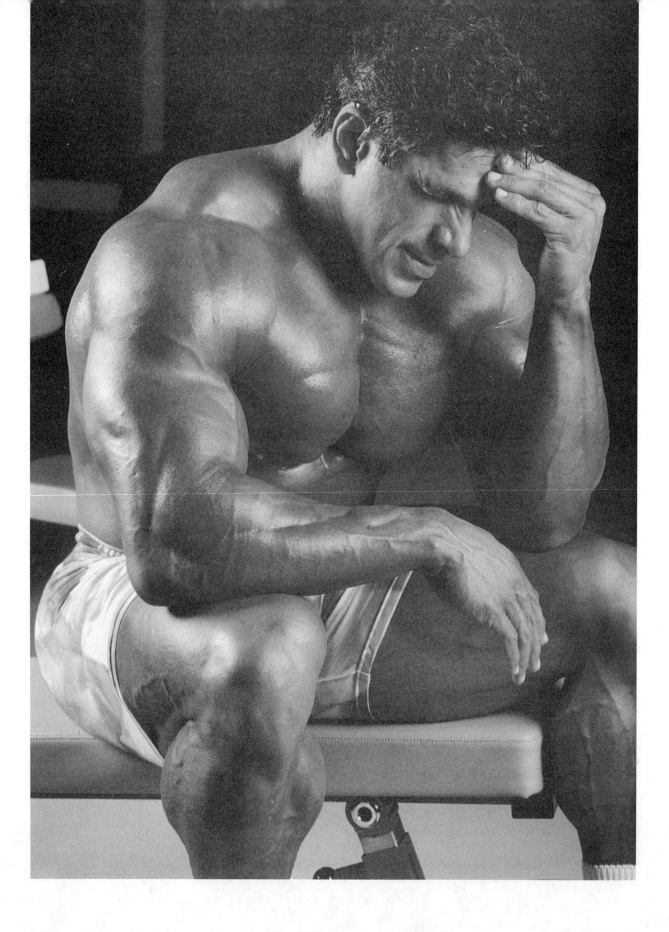

7
Life's Lessons:
Create Your Own Personal Power

Personal power is a concept that is frequently bandied about, but few people seem to actually know what it means. Fewer still know how to cultivate it themselves, let alone in others.

One of my friends is the world-renowned motivator Anthony Robbins. Believe me, this guy knows how to cultivate personal power! I first met Tony at a Christmas party in 1991. He walked up to me and said, "Mr. Ferrigno, I'm very impressed with what you've accomplished for yourself." What Tony and I have achieved is a drop in the bucket compared with what is truly possible if you direct your energies and belief systems in a positive manner.

Personal power, as I use the term, can be defined very simply: "personal" means yourself, while "power" means the ability to accomplish things by a force emanating from within yourself. So, your own "personal power" is how much control you are able to exert on yourself, your life, and your surroundings without letting yourself be affected by other people.

You have to be open to criticism, but you also have to have your own independent judgment of yourself and believe that only you can choose what's best for you. Anything that you want to do in life or achieve is attainable if and when you learn to tap into your own source of power deep within you. You can use it to take charge of every aspect of your life.

Let's say I want to go to the gym and curl a 100-pound dumbbell. Somebody there might say, "No, you can't curl that much weight. That's impossible." But, deep down, I know that I can. My mind has already said, "Yes, I can." Few things can waste your energy and time as efficiently as negativity. I dwell not on the weakness that others say I possess but on the successes I've already experienced. I look at the gains I've made in positive directions. I use my mind, not only to concentrate on the goals or obstacles but also to visualize the successful completion of the task before me. As a result, I always exercise with "full power," knowing that each successful repetition I perform is bringing me a step closer to my goal. During my workouts, I form a direct link between the muscle I'm training and my brain. The greater my focus on the task at hand, the greater my success in completing it. It's as simple as that.

Because of this strong, powerful, and personal belief, I know that I have the power to curl—and curl easily—those 100-pound dumbbells, with the result that when I grab hold of it, it's going to go up! If, however I had said to myself, "I can't do it" and didn't believe in my ability to lift that weight, then it just as surely wouldn't go up. My personal power would be weak. You can have weak personal power or you can have strong personal power, and only you can determine which flourishes within you. The important thing to remember is that you can change the quantity of personal power you possess. You are in charge of your own life.

I first learned that I possessed such power the day that I won the Mr. Universe competition. I realized then that if I could overcome the adversity of my life with my father —a man who would do anything he could to discourage me from weight training—and win the title, I possessed a very strong personal power and derived from it an equally strong belief in myself. If I used it right, nothing could stop me from achieving my goals.

I don't mean to imply that I just looked up and discovered this wonderful gift. I had had to take many often arduous steps to cultivate it. And I made my share of mistakes along the way. I fell on my face more often than I care to remember, but I kept getting back up until I had "learned to walk." I continued to take chances. It's not easy to change. In fact, changing your life may be the hardest thing in the world to do—but also the most rewarding. The key is to initiate change slowly, almost imperceptibly. Pretty soon, the change will be complete, and yet the process will have been so gradual that you never felt any imposition.

You've got to take chances in life. You've got to take risks. If you're afraid to do that, then you might as well forget it right now: close the book, walk away, and then go to work for someone else. Do what they tell you, rather than what you really want to, and give up on life. It's passed you by.

That's the truth. I'm not going to sugarcoat it for you, and I don't have a magic wand to make things otherwise. The thing is that we all know inside of us that we have the power to make a change for the better. It's our choice to cultivate that power or not.

Concentrate on Cultivating

Be patient. In time, you'll find the focus, and if you're a bodybuilder, exercises and workouts will become easier. Just relax and focus on your training. Sooner than you can imagine, you'll be making up your own routines, and you'll be in charge of not only your own body but your own life as well.

Sometimes people are in a bad environment. If you're in a family or a relationship with someone who has an alcohol or substance-abuse problem, you've got to make the choice to get out of it. You can't win fighting a war with losers because we live in a world that has more than its share of negativity. You have to understand that you are the only person who's 100 percent behind you. We come into this world by ourselves, and we'll be exiting it the same way, so you'd better make the most of life while there's still time to do it. When you die, you're not going to take a hundred people to the grave with you. It's only you—period. To feel good during your brief stay on this planet, cultivate friends who are positive and optimistic and who will assist you in forming a happy and productive life. Once again, it all comes down to your own choice to bring this about.

If someone near you wants to be negative, fine; simply move on with your life. Remember, you can't win with a team full of losers or negative thinkers. How people think is their choice; they choose to be either hopeful and optimistic or negative and pessimistic, and their lives reflect it. I know that if I had let my father take over my life or if I had listened to my jealous friends at school—as opposed to myself—I'd never be where I am today.

I want you to feel good about yourself too: emotionally, physically, and spiritually. All of us search in our own way for inner peace, but it must be remembered that the only tools you have to achieve it are yourself and your health. Your health is the result of your lifestyle decisions and must be tended to every day of your

life. And these lifestyle decisions are the direct result of your ability to cultivate your own personal power.

Whenever I mention this at a seminar, I am invariably asked, "Can *anybody* develop such personal power?" My answer is an unreserved "yes"—but the degree to which it's ultimately developed will vary with the individual and how hard he or she is willing to work at cultivating it. Some people have a severe lack of self-esteem, others have good self-esteem, and still others have extraordinarily high levels, but you have to know that its development will manifest at different rates in different people. It takes a long time for some to cultivate it, while others can do it seemingly overnight. It's just like weight training: it's not really the workout that's hard; it's motivating yourself to go to the gym or to get your weights at home set up and get started. That's the hardest part. Once you get started, I promise it will be easy, as with anything else; it gets easier the longer you stay with it. The first day is the hardest, but by the third day it's a little bit easier, and three days after that, it's easier still. The key is consistency. It's the common thread that connects every form of success.

If you want to better your life, you're going to have to make some extra effort to do something about it. It's not going to be easy, but you can take comfort in knowing it does get easier as you go along. You have to make a sacrifice. To get a Ph.D. in your field requires a sacrifice; you have to put in a lot of extra hours. The same principle applies if you want to be a champion bodybuilder. You do have to give up a lot to obtain the results you want.

Remember—It's Personal

One thing you have to give up is the notion that you want to achieve something in life in order to curry somebody else's approval. If you ever catch yourself doing that, you know you're in

trouble. That's what happened to me when I was young, but fortunately I was able to get out of that rut before it was too late. If you're concerned about satisfying someone other than yourself, then you'll never be truly satisfied, because nobody is going to care as much about your well-being as you do—nor should you expect anyone to.

A perfect example of this precept is Olympian swimmer Mark Spitz. In his life story, he wrote that he trained as hard as he did in swimming and won the seven gold medals at the Olympic games because of his father. He made a comeback a few years ago, but he didn't do so well in the competition. I talked to Mark recently, and I can report that he's a much happier man than he was during his Olympian days. He has a wife and children, and his life is fulfilled. He's the happiest that I've ever seen him. However, he was in denial when he was younger. Falling into the "pleasing other people" trap can happen to anybody. Many athletes have been known to stumble.

George Foreman is another who comes to mind. He's said that he was never happier than in his comeback bid because he was doing it for himself and not to please other people or fulfill their expectations. Sure, everybody is going to want his or her parents' approval to some degree, and that's fine, but don't make the mistake of *living for it*. You can compete only for and with yourself. If you compete for other people, you've lost the contest before it even starts.

My acquaintance with Tony Robbins, mentioned at the start of this chapter, underscores what I've been hammering home throughout this book about making the most of your own natural gifts, as well as keeping yourself open. You can learn something from anybody, if you're open to learn. Tony is where he is today because he was willing to work at cultivating his own personal power to make a positive change in his life. Likewise, I would still be in Brooklyn and miserable if I hadn't taken responsibility for my own life and gotten on a plane and headed to California and the better life that awaited me

there. My life changed and things started happening because *I made it happen*. That's personal power—and you have just as much of it as I do. Tony Robbins would tell you the same.

Take a Tip from Me

I hope that as you read about my life you'll look for ways in which my story can apply to you. Remember, you can get what you want out of life. Here's a tip. Write down a list—you don't have to show it to anyone—of what you want to achieve in life. Try to list beside each of your goals what you feel you will need to do in order to bring about its fulfillment. Choose me as a parallel if you like, and review and record the steps that I took to actualize my potential and cultivate my personal power. Then go for it! What's the worst that can happen? You're not going to go to jail, you're not going to die, and you're not going to get sick by attempting to improve the quality of your life. If you make a mistake, simply admit it and then choose an alternative. That's what makes personal power so much fun.

A related idea to begin your new quest is to keep a diary. Note daily the things that you've done to feel good about yourself (taking your children to school, understanding a difficult mathematical formula, improving some aspect of your physique). I always believe that if I do one thing each day to improve my knowledge or help someone, then I've accomplished a lot.

Track yourself over both the short and long term. Many people who diet, for instance, write down everything they eat so that they're able to better monitor their progress. You should do likewise with your feelings, exercises, and achievements. You'll soon be amazed by the gains you can achieve. To build a great body, you must have a sound mind. A firmly focused mind is 99.9 percent of the battle in achieving success in any walk of life.

You've got to be willing to risk the comfort of tradition every once in while if doing so yields the possibility of a better life. That's what life is all about. We're here for maybe 75 to 90 years; we're not here forever. So, if you want to make the best out of life, do the things that make it worthwhile for you.

For example, I like to live well. I like to have a nice house, I like being able to provide good food for my wife and children, and I like having the best home gym I can create. I made all of these things happen because they're all things I wanted to happen. It didn't fall from the trees; it wasn't just luck; I made all of these things happen. Training for the 1992 Mr. Olympia, I wanted to be in my best shape ever. It didn't happen by itself. I had to nearly kill myself to do it, but I made it happen. It's the same with anything else in life. You can have anything you want within your own capacity if you just take charge of your own destiny. Plus, you'll enjoy the accomplishments you achieve along the way.

Don't mistakenly assume that my methods will work only for people who, like me, come from a problem background or have had to leave home to be successful. If you happen to have parents who are supportive of you, that's fantastic. Maybe you can get your father or mother to join forces with you while you achieve your goals. But if you don't have that support, as in my case, choose your own path. You can blame only yourself for your own mistakes, and—there's no getting around it—you're going to make some. Just look at them as learning experiences, and keep pushing on. That's what makes a champion in any field.

And if you do have parents who support your endeavors, then, hey, my hat's off to you. It's good advice to get your dad and mom involved, because they can benefit from these principles just as surely as you can. In fact, they might even be able to take them a step further. Chances are that your father or mother is over 40, as I am. Let them take encouragement from what I've done. This way they can share their health and happiness with you. This book isn't meant only for people aged 18–35—it's for everyone, regardless of whether you're 9 or 90.

People at any age can do whatever they choose to do—as long as they have the belief that they can do it!

8
The Role of Family

Don't ever overlook the role that family plays in the grand scheme of success. I'm not going to prattle about how we should all learn to live together and love one another—that's not always a realistic goal—but we can take steps to ensure that the ones we choose to spend our lives with, marry, and bring into this world are loved, respected, and wanted.

For this to take place, however, we have to do a few things first. For one, we have to respect our partners, particularly the person we eventually decide to marry. Respect is crucial to the survival and healthy growth of a relationship. We must learn to consider our potential spouses not only our intellectual and emotional equals but also our partners in the purest sense of the term. So often, living in a predominantly old-world Italian neighborhood in Brooklyn, I'd see my friends' fathers telling their wives to "shut up," to "stay in the kitchen," and that "children should be seen but not heard." This is wrong— dead wrong! And if people hold to this warped credo, their emotional and mental development will likely suffer for it in the long run. No matter how big or strong you are, you need that other person.

Too much has been made of single-parent families and issues such as men's rights, women's rights, and so on. The only rights people are entitled to are those of opportunity and to be treated with human dignity. All the rest—respect, love, happiness, and so forth—have to be earned through your own conscious effort and reinforced by the choices you make. Believe me, you can be happy, you can have love, and you can be respected, but these qualities aren't available on demand.

Take my own life for example. Though I've criticized my father for what I consider his failings, I will say in his defense that he never was unfaithful to my mother, talked trash about her, or attempted to put her down in front of her children. That's to his credit. For all of their apparent differences, my mother and father were in many respects a perfect match. The same is true in my own marriage.

I met Carla one night in California when I was attempting to exercise a little of my newfound influence as a television personality. I was hoping to use my celebrity status to get myself and some friends into a filled-to-capacity eatery. The hostess had informed me that there were no seats available and that we'd have to wait at least 30 minutes. I protested that I was a busy guy with things to do and that waiting 30 minutes was out of the question, and I demanded to speak with

the manager. My request was granted, and two minutes later, Carla Green walked into my life. "What's the problem here?" she demanded. I could tell just by looking at her that she wasn't going to tolerate my B.S. for long. How right I was. After a minute of enduring my overdramatic lament, she told me to leave the premises! I was completely unprepared for that kind of response. I left the restaurant cursing under my breath at such gall! But in the back of my mind I was asking myself several telling questions, such as "Why would the manager of this restaurant not make room for a high-profile celebrity (after all, *The Incredible Hulk* was in its heyday)?" "Where did that manager get off talking to me like that?" and last but not least, "Who was that girl?" I was definitely intrigued.

The next week I found myself going back to that same restaurant. Showing up alone would have appeared too obvious, so I took a body-builder friend, Manuel Perry, with me. We sat down at a table and were preparing to order when, lo and behold, Carla Green spotted us and walked over to where we were sitting. She grabbed my arm and said, "How big are you? You got a seat this time, I see." Immediately I felt twinges of rejection starting to return to my life—until she flashed a smile at me! That smile! Man, I could feel my heart pound and sweat begin to flow from my brow. "Please, sit down with us," I said, barely able to get the words out, since I was concentrating on her beauty rather than on what I was trying to communicate. She smiled again and, to my surprise, agreed.

I can't even remember what we talked about, as I was totally lost in the ether of the moment. Here was the most beautiful, intelligent, and captivating woman I had ever seen, and more to the point, she seemed genuinely interested in me!

Summoning strength that even I didn't know I possessed, I screwed up the courage to ask her for her phone number. "I don't give my phone number out to customers," she said, but I took the look in her eyes to indicate that she wanted me to fish for an alternative. "All right," I countered, "I'll give you my phone number—and you

can call me whenever you feel like it." Carla was agreeable to that, and the next week she did call me. We could have gone anywhere on that first date and it would have been the greatest night of my life. I was so captivated that I knew right away I wanted to marry her.

We dated a little while longer before I popped the question. When Carla said yes, I felt a greater sense of worth than from all of the titles I'd won and all of the success I'd enjoyed to date! We were married nine months later, and we've been together ever since.

And here's my point: None of what I have accomplished in my life would have been nearly as meaningful nor as fulfilling had I continued to go it alone. Carla (and later the addition of our children) has given my life a sense of purpose and stability that I never would have been able to obtain otherwise. Finding that right person and creating children helps bring a sense of completeness to life.

Parts of a Whole

In all the years we've been married, I've never once second-guessed anything about Carla or my relationship with her. The late Bruce Lee once described his relationship with his wife Linda as "not a case of where 1 plus 1 equals 2, but rather that two halves fit snugly together to represent a whole." That perfectly describes my own feelings about being married to Carla. We have tremendous respect for each other, view ourselves as equals, and consider each other's opinion as carrying equal weight. Respect has deepened our love and devotion to each other. I would never do anything that would hurt, embarrass, or bring shame on either Carla or our relationship, and she feels the same way toward me.

When we decided to have children, this same philosophy was passed on to our progeny. Shanna, Louie Jr., and Brent are all treated respectfully, and their opinions count for something in our family. I learned from my own home experiences that kids have to believe that they're important and that both their mother and father think that their opinions (and the minds that formed them) are worth listening to.

To impart a feeling of self-respect and self-worth to our children is our primary concern as parents. Everything else, from financial security to material possessions, is secondary. I think we've been successful in this regard, and certainly our children are well adjusted. Whether or not they'll follow in their parents' vocational footsteps is up to them. All I know is that, whatever road they decide to take, they'll be assured of our total support every inch of the journey.

It's my firm belief that if more people would analyze their thoughts, wants, desires, and reasons for being involved in various relationships, there would be fewer divorces, fewer situations of spousal abuse, and fewer children brought into a family situation in which they're viewed as "inconveniences" or "accidents." What a terrible rap to lay on a defenseless child. After all, they never ask to be brought into this world. Parents bring them into it, and we had better damn well be prepared to provide for them—not just financially, but emotionally and supportively as well, from the moment they arrive.

Shared Rewards

Without a wife and children to share in my personal experiences and victories along the way, the spoils of life were bland and empty. When I won the Mr. Universe contest in Geneva, Switzerland, in 1973, I spent that night in a hotel room—alone! I never felt more confused or lonely in my life. I had no one with whom to share my proudest moment, and while I knew I had accomplished something, without someone I cared about to share it with, it didn't serve to make me very proud at all.

In contrast, when I competed in the 1992 and 1993 Mr. Olympia contests, Carla and all three of my children were present. Even though I didn't win either contest, I proved a point, and my family was there to see me do it. This feeling was a hundred times greater and more satisfying than the isolation and solitude I felt when I was crowned Mr. Universe.

In my opinion at least, meeting the right person and having children is a prerequisite to a complete life and total happiness. I've learned that with a wife and family behind you, you're a champion even if you've never won a competition in your life.

Part II

Bodybuilding for Everyone

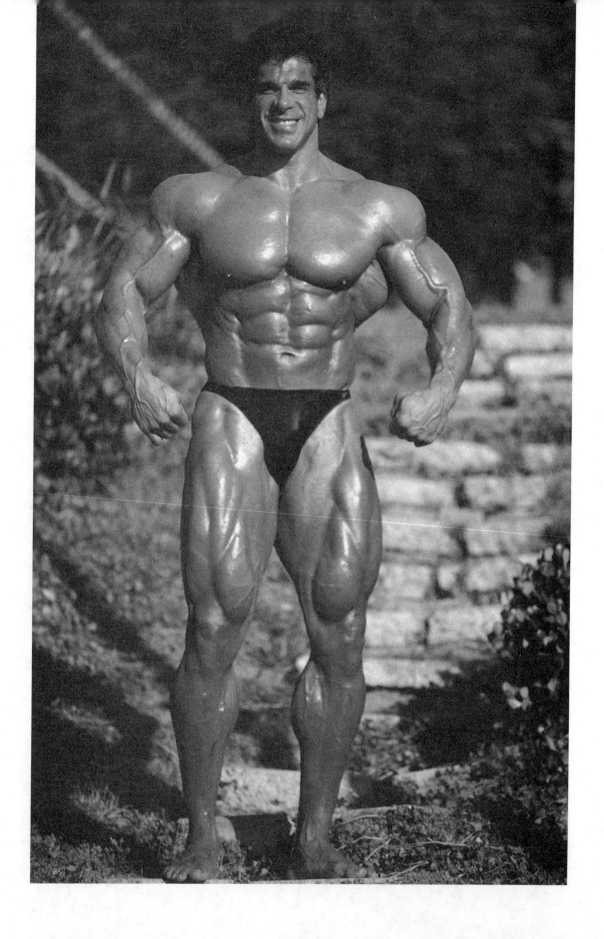

9
Introduction to Modern Bodybuilding

Anyone who takes up bodybuilding should begin with a general understanding of how lifting weights makes muscles grow and become stronger. The muscles of your body are made up of thousands of tiny muscle fibers that are composed completely of protein. The number of these fibers each individual has is determined by heredity. However, you can always improve on what nature gave you. Through adequate rest and proper nutrition, these tiny muscle fibers build up to become bigger and stronger, thus increasing muscle size and strength. So, it is essential that you eat properly and get plenty of rest.

A Sport for Serious Athletes

For years people have described bodybuilding as a warped sport for outcasts and muscle-bound freaks who do nothing but lift weights and look in mirrors all day. When I first began training, people frequently laughed at me, scorned me, and called me unflattering names. And at the front of the line was my own father, which didn't help matters. But with a burning desire to succeed, I went on to win the titles of Mr. America, Mr. International, and (twice) Mr. Universe.

More to the point, in the nationally televised Superstars competition in 1976, I placed fourth in the finals against some of the greatest athletes in the world. By doing so, I believed I showed the world that bodybuilders are true athletes in every sense of the word and can compete on an equal level with any other athlete. Today, when I walk down the street and people approach me to ask for my autograph, I feel proud and satisfied, and I realize that it's because of bodybuilding that I have become a success in life and a celebrity to the general public.

If you are going to succeed in improving your physique, you must have a positive attitude from the outset. Without that, you can never succeed in bodybuilding or, for that matter, in anything else in life. To succeed, you must truly believe in yourself and know that you will ultimately achieve the bodybuilding goals you have set.

Weight training can be whatever you want it to be. For years, coaches would not allow athletes to lift weights because they thought it made them muscle-bound. Now weight training is a main part of almost any team's training program. Nearly every great athlete in the world today engages in some type of weight training to improve his or her particular athletic abilities.

For example, runners must strengthen the muscles in their legs, shot-putters their arms and shoulders, and so on. Each individual has his or her own reason for weight training, be it strength, physical conditioning, athletic improvement, or just general all-around good health. Bodybuilders aren't the only ones who can benefit from weight training. Each of these ambitions can be fulfilled by following the instructions in the program that I prescribe here.

Whatever the reason you have chosen the sport of bodybuilding, the increase in your muscular size, strength, and endurance, as well as your flexibility, will amaze you. As your physique and general fitness begin to improve, you will constantly be striving to overcome new and different challenges and endeavors without fear of failure. The reason for your positive attitude will be your increased self-confidence, which will be brought about by your improved physique and ability. Your friends will be stunned by the changes they see in your appearance. You'll become the center of attention, admired and envied. In time, you may even be surprised to realize that people emulate you and seek your advice on health and strength.

All in Good Time

You will find that your greatest muscle gains will be made at the start of your training. But you *must* be guided through your early workouts to avoid injuries and keep muscle strains to a minimum. Training by trial and error is definitely out. Keep these cautionary rules in mind as you follow the program.

1. Haste makes waste. Exercises are explained in detail. Don't skip any steps, and don't rush the exercise.
2. Don't ever permit yourself to become discouraged. Too many bodybuilders with great potential become victims of poor motivation.

Do not be impatient; building muscles takes time.
3. Be persistent. Never give up. Remember, Rome wasn't built in a day. Bodybuilding can be compared to the erection of a building: you must develop a strong foundation that will withstand the constant punishment of heavy-weight workouts during the advanced stages. Careful, methodical training is essential during the early phases of any type of bodybuilding program.
4. Don't be in a hurry to increase weight; this can lead to unnecessary injuries and the loss of valuable time in your training progress.
5. In addition to your warm-up routine (see p. 70) always warm up your muscles with a light starting set before beginning your normal workout.

In regard to rest, you should try to get a minimum of eight hours of sleep each day. Try to be calm and relaxed at all times, since tension can also hamper muscular progress. Your workouts should be performed three times per week—either Monday, Wednesday, and Friday or Tuesday, Thursday, and Saturday. No more or less than this! By training every other day, you allow for proper recuperation of the muscle fibers that were broken down by the previous day's workout. Your actual muscle gains will be made on your rest days!

Be persistent; don't miss workouts. The more workouts you miss, the less your gains will be. Make up your mind to train three days a week no matter what happens. Now, let's get started!

In the exercise program that follows, you'll frequently encounter the terms *rep* and *set*. A rep is each repetition or movement that you do of an exercise. For instance, if you perform 10 sit-ups, then you have performed 10 reps (repetitions) of sit-ups. A set is a group of uninterrupted reps. Thus, 10 push-ups without pausing equals one set of 10 reps.

I have limited this chapter to seven basic exercises, which, when performed properly, should serve as the initial building blocks of a progressive weight-training program. These exercises are the squat, the bench press, the curl, the military press, the bent-over row, the calf raise, and the sit-up.

Following the descriptions of the exercises, you'll find an outline of an entire 32-week program, including the desired sets and reps for each exercise. And be sure to read the final instructions on warming up before starting your workouts.

Basic Exercises

The Squat

The squat is the most important and the most neglected exercise in weight training. Remember that you are only as strong as your legs. Many bodybuilders have lost crucial contests because of their underdeveloped legs. This exercise, when performed correctly, will not only develop the legs but also enlarge the rib cage, firm the area surrounding the hips and buttocks, and, most important, increase metabolism and promote breathing. With high reps, the squat will also tend to increase your weight because of the effect on your circulatory system.

For beginners, we'll concentrate on the full squat. You may perform this exercise flat-footed, but I recommend the use of a block of wood (2″ × 3″ or 2″ × 4″) placed under the heels. This will help you maintain your balance and will keep your back erect. Start with only the bar for form and technique and add 10 pounds each week to build strength.

To do this exercise, place the bar across your shoulders behind your neck, remembering to stand erect. Your feet should be in line with your shoulders, toes pointing outward. With the bar resting on your trapezius muscles (at the base of your neck), your chest and head up, and your eyes straight ahead, take a deep breath and slowly descend, remembering to keep strong tension on your thighs. Go down to a full squat with your buttocks almost touching your heels.

At this point, your back should be erect and your thighs parallel to the floor. It's important to *keep your back erect* throughout the exercise. This will prevent back injuries and will force your legs to carry the bulk of the weight to come back to the standing position. Do not bounce up, but rather gradually start your ascent by exhaling slowly as you come up to a standing position.

Important Points to Remember:
1. Head up, back erect, eyes straight ahead.
2. Slowly descend; do not collapse.
3. Start ascending as soon as your thighs are parallel to the floor.
4. Ascend slowly, placing tension on the thighs. Do not bounce, as this may cause knee injury.
5. Exhale as you rise slowly.
6. After a slight pause, descend again.
7. Try to perform these exercises in front of a mirror. This will enable you to study your form and leg development.

8. Most important, do not rush your reps and sets. Do not add additional weight until you are ready for it!

The Bench Press
The bench press builds massiveness into the pectorals (chest muscles). It is the most popular of all weight-training exercises.

The first thing to do is warm up with some light weight. This will help to prevent muscle pulls in the pectorals and will pump fresh blood into these muscles. The exercise also affects the front deltoid (shoulder) muscles.

Lying supine on a bench with your arms locked in front of you, slowly lower the bar until it touches the central portion of your pecs. Then, without bouncing, raise it again until your arms are once more in a locked position. Breathe in deeply as you lower the bar, and exhale as you raise it to the arms-locked position.

Important Points to Remember:
1. Warm up before the exercise.
2. Do not bounce the weight.
3. Never try to bench press with heavy weights by yourself. Always try to have somebody ready to grab the bar in case of an emergency, or perform the exercise in a power rack. (A power rack has adjustable pins, so if you're stuck it won't hurt your neck.)

The Standing Barbell Curl

Arms, particularly the biceps muscles, attract more attention than any other part of the body. I know that when I began bodybuilding, nothing interested me more than developing a pair of large, baseball-shaped biceps. My biceps are still my favorite body part, and no exercise develops the biceps better than the standing barbell curl.

Start the exercise with your feet wide apart, knees slightly bent, and your back straight. Grasp the bar with a shoulder-width grip, palms up. Keeping your arms extended, with the bar resting at your thighs and your back straight, curl the bar up to your shoulders. Then slowly lower the bar back down to the starting position, and repeat.

Do not swing the bar or bend your back in order to get the weight up. Inhale while curling the bar up, and exhale while lowering the bar.

Important Points to Remember:
1. Keep your back straight at all times.
2. Never swing the weight up.
3. Your palms should be kept facing up.
4. Your grip should be shoulder width.
5. Inhale when curling up (contracting) and exhale when curling down (extending).

The Military Press

Developing broad shoulders is one of the greatest assets for an athlete. Whatever the sport in which you intend to excel, broad and powerful shoulders are one of the most important physical characteristics you can have.

A combination of the bench press and the military press will strongly benefit the massive development of the pectoral and deltoid muscles. I still include the military press in my training program because of the benefits I receive in my triceps and for complete shoulder development.

With your palms facing downward, raise the barbell to your chest and take a deep breath while maintaining the position of locked knees and hips. Then raise the barbell overhead until your elbows are in a locked position. For greater gains to the deltoids, concentrate on maintaining tension in this position. Lower the bar back to your chest, exhaling while you perform the movement. Remember to lower the bar slowly for greater benefits.

Important Points to Remember:
1. Have knees and hips locked prior to the lift.
2. Concentrate on maintaining tension while lowering the weight.

The Bent-Over Barbell Row

By far the most important group of back muscles to every bodybuilder is the latissimus dorsi group, or the lats as we call them in the trade. Huge, bulky lats give the entire physique a broad, massive appearance, as well as the much desired "V" shape to your back. To develop powerful lats that possess corresponding shape and bulk, there is no better exercise than the bent-over barbell row.

The bent-over row is performed by starting with your feet shoulder-width apart and your knees slightly bent. Bend forward at the waist and grasp the barbell with your palms down in a grip that is slightly wider than shoulder width. Keeping your back flat and your arms fully extended, pull the weight up to your chest. Do not swing or move your upper body. Hold the bar at your chest for two seconds, then slowly and steadily lower the bar down to the starting position. Breathe in when you bring the bar up, and breathe out when lowering the bar.

Important Points to Remember:

1. Keep your back flat at all times.
2. Keep knees slightly bent.
3. Bring the bar to your chest, then lower it slowly.
4. Do not swing or move your upper body.
5. Inhale when bringing the bar up, and exhale when lowering the bar.

The Calf Raise

Most bodybuilders train and develop larger chests, shoulders, and arms, but for some strange reason, many ignore their calves. A perfectly developed calf is shaped like a diamond and will add highlight, proportion, and symmetry to your overall physique. Without proper calf development, your physique will be unbalanced, out of proportion, and at best incomplete.

The calf raise is the finest exercise there is for developing large, diamond-shaped calves. Begin by placing your feet on the blocks; brace yourself with your arms and rest your lower back against the machine. Next, move the balls of your feet so that your heels hang off the foot blocks. Keeping your back straight, simply raise up on your toes as high as you can go, hold the contraction for two seconds, then lower yourself back to the starting position. As you perform your reps, be sure to inhale when raising and exhale when lowering.

To do calf raises with a barbell, place the barbell on your shoulders and keep your feet shoulder-width apart. Proceed with the same movements as described for the calf raise machine.

The exercise should be performed with a slow, deliberate movement. The amount of weight you can handle is not the most important element in performing calf raises. Your concentration should be on maximum contraction and stretch.

Important Points to Remember:

1. Keep your back straight at all times.
2. Rise as high on your toes as possible. Hold for two seconds.
3. Slowly lower yourself on all repetitions.

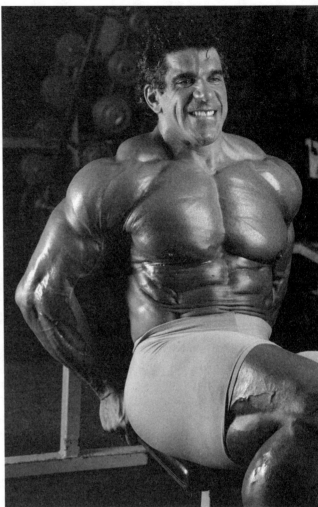

The Twisting Bent-Knee Sit-Up

For the beginner as well as the most advanced bodybuilder, a muscular and trim waist is an absolute must. The midsection is one of the most vital zones of your body. For super health and an athletic appearance, the waist should be trim and strong, with the abdominal muscles fully developed. The abdominal muscles consist of the rectus abdominis and the external obliques. The twisting bent-knee sit-up develops both of these muscle groups.

Begin this exercise by lying on your back with your feet anchored securely to the floor and your knees slightly bent. With your hands clasped firmly behind your neck, sit up and touch your right elbow to your left knee. Slowly lower yourself back to the starting position, and repeat—this time touching your left elbow to your right knee. Return to the starting position and repeat for the prescribed number of repetitions and sets listed in the beginner's course that follows. Exhale forcibly through tightly compressed lips when sitting up, and inhale when lowering your body.

Important Points to Remember:
1. Feet should be anchored securely to the floor.
2. The right elbow goes to the left knee, and the left elbow to the right knee.
3. Lower yourself slowly.

The Beginner's Course

This week you should gradually increase the resistance by adding more weight (2.5 pounds) and reps (two) to each exercise.

Week 1		
Squats	1 set	10 reps
Bench Presses	1 set	8 reps
Military Presses	1 set	8 reps
Bent-Over Rows	1 set	8 reps
Curls	1 set	8 reps
Calf Raises	1 set	8 reps
Sit-Ups	1 set	12 reps

During the first week, for each exercise you should use a weight that is easy for the prescribed number of repetitions. Each week thereafter, you should add moderate weight (between 2.5 and 5 pounds) until the load is heavy enough so that you can do no more than the desired number of sets and reps for each exercise. After that, whenever you can do more reps than prescribed without sacrificing good exercise form, add weight and continue with the prescribed number of reps. However, if you find you cannot do the desired number of reps when you add weight, stay with the weight you were using until the desired number of reps and sets becomes easy. Then, and only then, should you add weight. Never add weight at the expense of exercise form. Be patient; your strength will come along in due time.

Week 3		
Add 2.5 pounds to every exercise except the sit-up.		
Squats	2 sets	10 reps
Bench Presses	2 sets	8 reps
Military Presses	2 sets	8 reps
Bent-Over Rows	2 sets	8 reps
Curls	2 sets	8 reps
Calf Raises	2 sets	12 reps
Sit-Ups	2 sets	15 reps

This week you increase the resistance by doing two sets for each exercise. Keep this important step in mind: you'll perform one set of 10 reps of squats, rest two minutes, and then perform another set of 10 reps of squats. Remember, always rest two minutes between each set of squats. All other exercises require only one minute of rest between sets.

Week 2		
Add 2.5 pounds to every exercise except the sit-up.		
Squats	1 set	12 reps
Bench Presses	1 set	10 reps
Military Presses	1 set	10 reps
Bent-Over Rows	1 set	10 reps
Curls	1 set	10 reps
Calf Raises	1 set	10 reps
Sit-Ups	1 set	14 reps

Week 4		
Add 2.5 pounds to every exercise except the sit-up.		
Squats	2 sets	12 reps
Bench Presses	2 sets	10 reps
Military Presses	2 sets	10 reps
Bent-Over Rows	2 sets	10 reps
Curls	2 sets	10 reps
Calf Raises	2 sets	15 reps
Sit-Ups	2 sets	20 reps

This week you have progressively increased the resistance by again adding weight and repetitions.

Weeks 5 Through 10

Squats	3 sets	10 reps
Bench Presses	3 sets	8 reps
Military Presses	3 sets	8 reps
Bent-Over Rows	3 sets	8 reps
Curls	3 sets	8 reps
Calf Raises	3 sets	15 reps
Sit-Ups	3 sets	25 reps

Notice that I did not tell you to add weight. By this time, you should be the best judge of that. If the weight you are using for the exercise is easy for the prescribed number of sets and reps, add weight accordingly. On the other hand, if you are just able to make the prescribed number of sets and reps, then do not add weight. Note, however, that we have increased the number of sets to three for each exercise.

Weeks 11 Through 16

Squats	4 sets	12 reps
Dumbbell Bench Presses	4 sets	8 reps
Dumbbell Military Presses	4 sets	8 reps
Dumbbell Bent-Over Rows	4 sets	8 reps
Dumbbell Curls	4 sets	8 reps
Calf Raises	4 sets	15 reps
Sit-Ups	4 sets	25 reps

As you can see, we have progressively increased resistance by working up to four sets for each exercise. However, we have now substituted dumbbells for barbells on some of the exercises. After training with the same exercises over a long period of time, your muscles as well as your mind become stale. When this happens, neither responds as quickly as previously. This change of pace will add enthusiasm and variety to your workouts and will guarantee continued progress on your bodybuilding program. The dumbbell exercises are performed the same way as the barbell exercises.

Remember to use a weight for each exercise that will allow you to work hard on the prescribed number of sets. Always maintain good form on each exercise and add weight when you find the given number of sets and reps to be easy.

Months 4 Through 6

Squats	5 sets	12 reps
Barbell Bench Presses	5 sets	8 reps
Barbell Military Presses	5 sets	8 reps
Barbell Bent-Over Rows	5 sets	8 reps
Barbell Curls	5 sets	8 reps
Calf Raises	5 sets	15 reps
Sit-Ups	5 sets	25–30 reps

Notice that we have increased our sets to five and have gone back to using barbell exercises. The reason for returning to the barbell is again to prevent staleness and boredom in your workouts. You should have noticed by now that the calf and abdominal muscles respond best to higher reps.

Months 7 and 8

Squats	6 sets	12 reps
Dumbbell Bench Presses	6 sets	8 reps
Dumbbell Military Presses	6 sets	8 reps
Dumbbell Bent-Over Rows	6 sets	8 reps
Dumbbell Curls	6 sets	8 reps
Calf Raises	6 sets	15 reps
Sit-Ups	6 sets	30 reps

For the final eight weeks of this course, we return again to dumbbells for the bench press, curl, military press, and bent-over row. This change will help as always in keeping up your interest and motivation. Also, you'll now perform six sets for each exercise, remembering to perform each exercise with good form and adequate rest between sets.

This completes your "getting started" beginner's routine. If you diligently follow the instruc-

tions I have given in regard to sets, reps, proper rest, and exercise form, along with persistence (i.e., not missing any workouts), then you are well on your way to good health and a super physique.

Follow this routine exactly the way I have instructed, progressing gradually over the full 32-week period.

Warm Up Before You Work Out

It's such a simple thing to do, and yet many athletes and bodybuilders will be injured this year by not taking the time to warm up properly. I can't stress the importance of this enough: always warm up thoroughly before your workout. Warming up not only promotes fluidity in your joints and connective tissues, but also lessens the chances of trauma to muscle tissue.

You don't, however, need to turn your warm-up into a workout. Spend 8–10 minutes on either a stationary bike, treadmill, or stairclimber until you get a slight sweat going, your heart rate is up into its training zone (220 minus your age equals your maximum heart rate, and your training zone is 65 to 80 percent of that), and your muscles are warm.

Then it's time to stretch. Stretching before a workout does two important things. First, it sends a signal to your muscles that they're about to receive stimulation; second, proper stretching raises your body temperature, a good way to decrease the risk of overuse injuries. Perform each stretch smoothly—no bouncing or jerking. Hold for a minimum of 6 to 10 seconds per rep. As you get more comfortable with these exercises, you can attempt to hold the stretch for 20 to 30 seconds.

Stretches
Pectoral/Shoulder Stretch
Stand sideways next to a pole. With your right hand around the support and your left hand against your chest, gradually lean away from the pole. Feel the stretch in your chest and shoul-

ders, hold this position for 10 seconds, relax, and repeat three times. Switch sides and repeat.

Quadriceps Stretch

Sit on your heels and gently lean backward, supporting your weight with your hands. Gradually lean farther back, relaxing your tight quads as you do so. Hold the stretch, relax, and repeat.

Hamstring Stretch

From a seated position, spread your legs apart and gently pull your chest closer to your knees. Do this slowly, without bouncing. Hold the stretch, and then repeat for the desired number of reps.

Adding Aerobics

Here are a few pointers on balancing your weight training with an aerobic regimen, which I highly recommend.

- Perform your aerobic or recreational sports activities—swimming, running, tennis, cycling, whatever—three or four times per week for 20 to 30 minutes per session.
- Do these activities after your workout, not before. This is especially important when you plan to train your legs. Pre-exhausting your legs before doing squats will limit the effectiveness of your workouts.
- Use a day off from weight training to focus on cardio exercises. You'll have more time and pursue your sport with more energy and with less chance of injuring your joints and tendons.
- Vary the activity. Instead of, say, riding a stationary bike after every workout, try to alternate the bike with 20 minutes on a treadmill or on a stairclimber.

10
My Best Mass and Power Course

Gaining muscular body weight and strength is unquestionably not an easy task. It is, however, possible to gain both muscle mass and strength at an impressive rate of speed if you go about it correctly. I started training at age 12 at a height of 5'5" and a weight of barely 120 pounds. I was so weak that I couldn't bench press more than 65 pounds!

Now, 32 years later, I weigh 180 pounds more, and I'm in top muscular condition. And even though I've never specialized in pure strength training, I can bench well over 420 pounds for reps and perform leg presses with more than 2,000 pounds!

Gaining muscular mass and strength requires a combination of four very important factors: proper training, proper nutrition, sufficient recuperation time, and the correct mental attitude.

By following my suggestions in these areas, you'll be able to gain both strength and all the muscle mass your frame can carry.

Training the Right Way

At the most basic level, it's necessary to gain strength in order to gain mass. It's that simple; get stronger, and you'll get bigger. There's a direct correlation between the amount of weight you use in your exercises and the size of the muscles that lift it. The more you lift in the bench press and squat, for example, the bigger your muscles will become in the regions of your pecs and legs.

Don't think that because one individual who has 15" arms can bench press 400 pounds, while another individual with 17" arms can bench only 350 pounds, that size and strength aren't connected. You can't compare individuals. The first fellow may have a more favorable tendon attachment or shorter upper-arm bones, which tend to give you more leverage. The only person with whom you can compare yourself in terms of making progress is yourself, and you will get bigger only when you get stronger.

While using heavier weights for reps in your workouts means you increase muscle size, it takes a low number of reps and extremely heavy weights to build the ligament and tendon power that assures you of great strength. Thus, small men with great muscle-attachment strength are able to easily outlift bigger men who haven't trained specifically for muscle power.

Weight-gaining workouts have to be tailored to your metabolism. Slow gainers—who usually

73

have very fast metabolic rates—generally have to train less frequently than fast gainers. Slow gainers tend to run their energy reserves too low in longer workouts. Then they can't recuperate enough between workouts to grow, so they often overtrain and actually begin to lose muscle size.

Recuperation plays a vital role in how fast you gain, and it's essential that your workouts be tailored to fit your recuperative abilities. I could write an entire book on the relationship between recuperation and weight gain, but I'll give you the highlights a little later in this chapter.

As you may have been able to surmise, you'll need short and heavy workouts to gain weight: heavy to stimulate growth, short to allow recuperation as well as growth. The easiest way to perform short workouts is to restrict them to basic exercises that work two or more large muscle groups at the same time. Flyes, for example, are much less effective as a chest exercise for muscle growth and strength increases than bench presses. Flyes isolate resistance only in the pecs, while benches work the pecs, delts, and triceps (plus the lats, to some extent) simultaneously.

To train heavy and short on basic exercises, I recommend that you "pyramid" your poundages. This involves using heavier weights and lower reps on each successive set (e.g., bench press: 135 × 12; 205 × 10; 255 × 8; 305 × 6; 340 × 4; 360 × 2). This allows you to warm up thoroughly and still use the heaviest possible weights for each movement.

Combining all of the foregoing principles, the following is my best mass and power routine for hard gainers. I recommend that you perform this workout on Mondays, Wednesdays, and Fridays. I have asterisked (*) the exercises in which you should pyramid your poundages.

You should be able to do this routine in one hour or less. If it takes longer, you're most likely resting more than 60–75 seconds between sets, which can allow your body to cool off and leave you more vulnerable to injuries.

If you're a beginner—that is, if you have trained less than six months—the full mass and power routine would be appropriate for you. If

Hard Gainers Mass and Power Routine		
Exercise	**Sets**	**Reps**
Sit-Ups	1	25–40
Squats	5	12/10/8/6/4*
Deadlifts	1	6–8
Barbell Bent-Over Rows	5	12/10/8/6/4*
Shrugs	1	10–15
Bench Presses	5	12/10/8/6/4*
Military Presses	1	6–8
Barbell Curls	1	6–8
Calf-Machine Raises	3	15/12/10

you have trained less than six weeks, however, do only the first three sets of each exercise marked for pyramiding.

If you're a more advanced trainee, you might want to try the following four-day split routine, which is my personal mass and power program. Never train more than four days per week on a weight-gain routine. Again, pyramid your weights on the reps marked with an asterisk.

The preceding routine is good for developing strength, but for maximum power, you'll need to do fewer reps. Try doing pyramids of 5/4/3/2/1 reps on the basic exercises marked with an asterisk. Once every two weeks, you can do a rest-pause routine of five sets of single reps on each of the exercises marked for pyramiding.

Sleep and Rest

Recuperation is a prerequisite to muscle growth, and the primary way your body recuperates is through sleep and rest. If you were to compare your recuperative balance to your checking account, workouts would be checks drawn or "withdrawals," and sleep and rest would represent deposits. Of course, you should have

Four-Day Split Routine

Monday and Thursday

Exercise	Sets	Reps
Sit-Ups	1	25–50
Squats	5	12/10/8/6/4*
Leg Extensions	3	8–10
Deadlifts	3	10/8/6*
Barbell Bent-Over Rows	5	12/10/8/6/4*
Lat Pulldowns	5	12/10/8/6/4*
Shrugs	3	10–15
Barbell Curls	4	10/8/6/6*
Dumbbell Curls	4	10/8/6/6*
Wrist Curls	4	10–15
Standing Calf Raises	5	10–15

Tuesday and Friday

Exercise	Sets	Reps
Leg Raises	1	25–50
Bench Presses	5	12/10/8/6/4*
Incline Presses	5	12/10/8/6/4*
Military Presses	4	12/10/8/6*
Upright Rows	4	12/10/8/6*
Lying Triceps Extensions	4	6–8
Triceps Pushdowns	4	6–8
Seated Calf-Machine Raises	5	10–15

enough deposits to cover your checks or you'll go broke (i.e., overtrain).

The amount of sleep needed varies widely from individual to individual, but it usually falls in the range of 8 to 10 hours a night. I'd recommend that you get as much sleep as possible. You can even take a half-hour nap in the afternoon, if that doesn't keep you awake at night. Remember, your muscles grow during rest, not during training sessions.

Besides sleep, rest is also essential, particularly if you're a hard gainer. Limit your physical activities strictly to bodybuilding until you reach your muscle mass goals. A lot of champion bodybuilders run before contests, but you should never do that until you are in a cutting-up phase and striving for maximum definition. If you want to look like a bodybuilder, bodybuild; if you want to look like a runner, run.

As a final component of the recuperation cycle, always try to keep your mind tranquil. If you're constantly nervous and worried about something, your body is burning up tremendous amounts of nervous energy. Such energy should be directed instead into training and recuperation. So, try to plug the energy leaks by staying calm and tranquil.

You Can Do It

If there's been one overriding theme to this book, it's that nothing is possible unless you truly believe it's possible. The mind is that powerful, and most top bodybuilders call the mind their strongest muscle.

In essence, your mental attitude must be totally positive. You must believe you can succeed, and you can with the training, dieting, and recuperative advice in these pages.

I suggest that you also practice the technique of visualization. Each night before you fall asleep, vividly imagine yourself the way you want to be. This triggers a psychological mechanism called the self-fulfilling prophecy, which allows your mind to program you to achieve the image you've visualized. Not bad for 10–15 minutes of concentrated daydreaming before you fall asleep!

Gain Muscle, Not Fat

When I was 19, I went from 220 pounds all the way up to 315—a full 95 pounds—in seven months of heavy training and all-day eating. This may seem like a highly desirable gain, but a lot of fat came with that muscle. At 315, I had

several spare tires around my waist. And when I got back into contest shape six months later—after a great struggle, I might add—I weighed only 221. That's an effective gain of only one pound in more than a year!

Believe me, bulking up and training down is not an effective way to gain muscle mass. Over the years, I've discovered that I can't go more than 8–10 pounds over my contest weight and still retain maximum muscle mass once I train down. I consider bulking up and training down a total and foolish waste of time for most body-builders.

As you gain weight, keep an eye on your abdominals. As soon as they blur out—particu-larly the intercostals (muscles located between the ribs) and lower abdominals—you'll know you're getting too fat. Reduce your caloric intake and harden back up. It's best in the long run to gain weight slowly and patiently so that it's all muscle, rather than to merely pork up as I did years ago.

In the final analysis, you're the one who will benefit from using this program regularly and to the best of your training ability. Push hard in your training, add to your poundages whenever you can, never miss a workout, eat correctly, think positively, and sleep and rest enough for full recuperation. If you do, you'll be a lot bigger and stronger at this time next year.

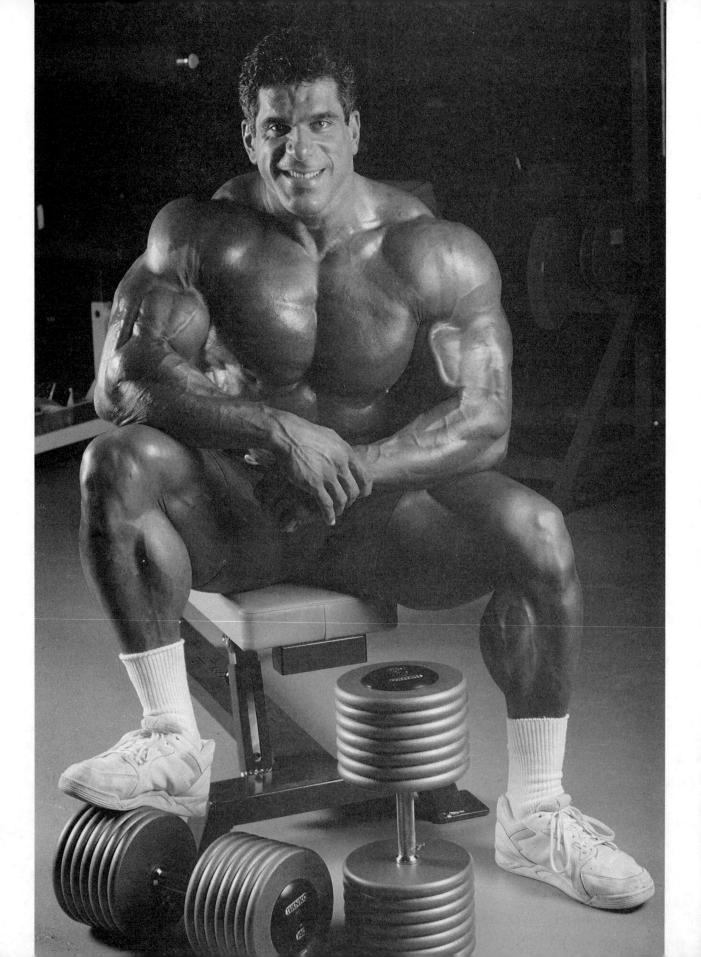

11
Training for Any Body Type

According to scientist W. H. Sheldon's classic study of somatotypes, human body types can be divided into three general classes: *ectomorphs*, *endomorphs*, and *mesomorphs*. Each of these three major body types demands a unique training and dietary approach for maximum success in gaining weight.

Determining Your Body Type

To help place you within the body-type grouping that you most closely resemble, descriptions of the three major categories follow.

Ectomorphs
Ectomorphs are long and lean, built for endurance more than strength. Their metabolism is high, so high in fact that they can eat huge amounts of food without any danger of gaining fat. For some, of course, this would be bliss, but for aspiring bodybuilders it's a flat-out curse. Because they have such high metabolic rates, ectomorphic bodybuilders frequently experience incredible difficulties in gaining weight.

Endomorphs
An endomorph is sluggish, naturally fat, and, typically, not athletic at all. People in this category can put on weight easily, but most of it is fat. The endomorph invariably experiences difficulty achieving good muscular definition. With a proper diet and effective training, however, endomorphs can combine muscle size with good density.

Mesomorphs
A mesomorph is a natural bodybuilder, with a frame and metabolism ideally suited for gaining muscle. This type is usually characterized by shorter and more powerful arms and legs than ectomorphic individuals, as well as a longer torso. Mesomorphs are built for speed and power. They usually don't have difficulty gaining weight, but if they're not careful with their diet, this weight can include a high portion of fat.

Weighing In

Ectomorphs and Weight Gain
Regardless of body type, it takes plenty of exercise with heavy weights to increase muscle size.

Indeed, there is a direct correlation between strength and muscle girth. In other words, the heavier the weights you use, the larger will be your muscle size.

Ectomorphic bodybuilders must be careful to not overtrain, since they are prone to do so. Overtraining will quickly halt any muscle gains dead in their tracks. Since I can't physically climb into your body to see how it feels, you'll need to make decisions on your own about the number of sets you perform in your training, but consider my guidelines. Ectomorphs can make their best gains on three to six heavy sets per body part, depending on how experienced they are. Bear in mind that even the most experienced bodybuilders who are ectomorphic could overtrain on more than six sets per body part, merely sharpening their physiques instead of building them. With less than three months of training, three sets per body part would be most appropriate (add one more set of each exercise per six months of training, up to six sets of each).

Here's a suitable beginning workout for an ectomorph with an eye toward size.

Ectomorph Mass-Gaining Routine
Monday/Wednesday/Friday

Exercise	Sets	Reps
Sit-Ups	1	25–50
Standing Calf Raises	3	15/12/10
Squats	3	10/8/6
Stiff-Legged Deadlifts	1	10–15
Bent-Over Rows	3	10/8/6
Shrugs	2	10–15
Bench Presses	3	10/8/6
Military Presses	3	10/8/6
Lying Triceps Extensions	3	10/8/6
Barbell Curls	3	10/8/6
Wrist Curls	1	10–15

On exercises for which I've recommended a range of reps—10–15 or 25–50—do a number of repetitions within that range. The "10/8/6" simply means that you should perform one set of 10 reps, add weight and do one set of 8, and add weight again for a set of 6. The weight jumps should be roughly 15–20 percent between sets. So, if you use 100 pounds for your first set of squats, the second would be with 120 and the third with 140.

It's essential to push hard to steadily increase exercise poundages, because of the relationship between strength and muscle size. The final repetition of the third set should be absolutely the last rep you can do. Only by going close to failure like this can you be assured of getting the most out of each exercise.

While the final set should be performed to the maximum, the sets leading up to it can be at 75–90 percent of max. They are for building muscle, to a certain degree, but are more to warm up your muscles and joints for the all-out final set. Without a good warm-up, it would be possible to injure yourself. You will also not be able to thoroughly stimulate your muscles with the final set unless fully warmed up.

It's difficult for me to tell you how fast you should be progressing, because every individual moves forward at a different rate. While you may progress more quickly or slowly, in general you should be able to increase leg and back exercises by about five pounds per week and exercises for other body parts by five pounds every other week.

In addition to proper exercise, ectomorphs should be conscious of their diets. As I'll explain in more detail later in this book, it's necessary to take in more calories than your body needs when gaining weight.

Because of their unusually high metabolism, long, thin muscles, and light bone structure, ectomorphs can seemingly ingest tons of calories and still not gain weight. This creates a problem, because they can consume even large quantities of junk foods (ice cream, cake, soft drinks, hamburgers, etc.) without gaining weight.

The best nutritional alternative is to consume a balanced diet that is 10 to 15 percent higher in calories than what is needed to maintain a constant body weight. In addition, it will be necessary to eat four to six smaller meals per day, rather than the traditional two or three larger ones. This is a logical procedure, since the human body can digest and utilize only 20 to 30 grams of protein every two to three hours.

Here's one diet that has worked wonders with everyone I know who's tried it.

Meal One (8 A.M.)
Cooked whole-grain cereal with raw milk and honey
One or two pieces of fruit, or juice
Small piece of meat or fish
Supplements

Meal Two (11 A.M.)
Steak and eggs
Potato or rice dish
Raw milk
Supplements

Meal Three (1 P.M.)
Chicken or fish
Salad
Cottage cheese
Raw milk
Supplements

Meal Four (4 P.M.)
Protein milkshake
Supplements

Meal Five (7 P.M.)
Beef or ham
Potato or rice dish
Vegetable
Raw milk
Supplements

Meal Six (10 P.M.)
Yogurt or hard cheese
Fruit or juice
Supplements

Lactose Intolerance

Some individuals cannot tolerate milk, or more specifically the sugar chemical called lactose within it. In such cases, I recommend fruit or vegetable juices in place of the milk.

Protein Milkshake

I'll discuss the key weight-gaining supplements later in this chapter, but for now you should know how to mix the protein shake mentioned in Meal Four. Pour about 10 ounces of raw whole milk into a blender. Raw milk is better for weight gain than pasteurized milk because pasteurization heat denatures milk's protein. You can buy raw milk in most health-food stores.

In your blender, you should also put three heaping tablespoons of milk-and-egg protein powder. You can add one or two soft-boiled eggs if you like, but don't use raw eggs. The B vitamin called biotin is destroyed by the chemical reactions of raw eggs. If you want to use eggs in your protein shake, boil them for about one-and-a-half to two minutes first.

Finally, you can throw in some type of natural flavoring as well, but stay away from artificial concoctions, such as chocolate syrup, etc. Bananas and strawberries are my favorite fruit flavorings in a protein drink, but you can use almost any type of fruit. Just be sure to run the blender long enough to evenly distribute the tiny fruit pieces throughout the shake.

Endomorphs and Weight Gain

For endomorphs the bodybuilding training to gain muscle mass can include more sets than the ectomorph performs. Six to 10 sets per body part would be not only normal for endomorphs but also appropriate to keep from overtraining.

When you work your way up to the higher number of sets, I recommend that you train four days per week on a split routine, doing each major body part twice per week.

Here's a good endomorph mass-gaining routine.

Endomorph Mass-Gaining Routine

Monday and Thursday

Exercise	Sets	Reps
Sit-Ups	1	50–100
Standing Calf Raises	4	15–20
Seated Calf Raises	4	15–20
Squats	6	15/12/10/8/6/6
Stiff-Legged Deadlifts	3	15–20
Shrugs	4	10–15
Bent-Over Rows	4	12/10/8/6
Bent-Arm Pullovers	4	12/10/8/6
Barbell Curls	4	8–12
Wrist Curls	4	15–20

Tuesday and Friday

Exercise	Sets	Reps
Leg Raises	1	50–100
Bench Presses	6	15/12/10/8/6/4
Incline Presses	4	12/10/8/6
Presses Behind Neck	4	12/10/8/6
Upright Rows	4	12/10/8/6
Lying Triceps Extensions	4	8–12
Standing Triceps Extensions	4	8–12
Reverse Wrist Curls	4	15–20
Neck Strap	4	15–20
Donkey Calf Raises	4	15–20
Leg-Press Calf Raises	4	15–20

As with all weight-gain programs, be sure to steadily increase the weights you use.

Endomorphs must walk a dietary tightrope, balancing between consuming just enough calories to gain muscle weight and too many calories, which will increase fat levels. In general, endomorphs will eat far less than ectomorphs while gaining muscle mass. The protein levels should be as high, but there must be considerably less carbohydrate and fat.

Using a four-meal-per-day plan, here is a good endomorphic muscle-mass diet.

Meal One (8 A.M.)
Cheese omelet
Cottage cheese
Tea or coffee (with artificial sweetener)
Supplements

Meal Two (Noon)
Tuna salad
Nonfat raw milk
Piece of fruit
Supplements

Meal Three (4 P.M.)
Chicken
Salad
Iced tea (with artificial sweetener)
Supplements

Meal Four (7:30 P.M.)
Turkey
Salad
Vegetables
Diet soda
Supplements

In general, it is best to not eat later than three hours before bedtime, since excess calories can't be burned off while you're sleeping. If you're eating too late, the extra calories are merely deposited as fat throughout your body.

Within a short time, you can develop an instinctive awareness of how many calories you should be taking in each day. If you feel fuller and fatter one day, or perhaps lethargic in your workout, you've likely eaten too much. On the other hand, if your body-fat levels are staying constant or going down, and your muscle mass is increasing, you'll know you have consumed the correct amount of calories.

Mesomorphs and Weight Gain

The training program for weight-gaining mesomorphs is about halfway between the workouts of ectomorphs and endomorphs. Here is a good four-day split routine.

Mesomorph Mass-Gaining Routine
Monday and Thursday

Exercise	Sets	Reps
Sit-Ups	1–3	50–100
Donkey Calf Raises	4	10–15
Seated Calf Raises	3	10–15
Squats	6	15/12/10/8/6/4
Stiff-Legged Deadlifts	3	10–15
Upright Rows	4	12/10/8/6
Seated Pulley Rows	4	12/10/8/6
Nautilus Pullovers	4	12/10/8/6
Preacher Curls	4	12/10/8/6
Alternate Dumbbell Curls	3	10/8/6
Dumbbell Wrist Curls	4	15–20

Tuesday and Friday

Exercise	Sets	Reps
Leg Raises	1–3	50–100
Standing Calf Raises	4	10–15
Leg-Press Calf Raises	3	10–15
Incline Presses	4	12/10/8/6
Dumbbell Bench Presses	4	12/10/8/6
Military Presses	4	10/8/6/4
Bent Laterals	3	8–12
Lat Pushdowns	4	8–12
Dumbbell Triceps Extensions	3	8–12
Reverse Curls	3	8–12
Neck Strap	4	15–20

If you can't do one or more of the exercises in this workout due to lack of equipment, feel free to substitute any other basic exercise for the same muscle group.

Of the three major somatotypes, mesomorphs have the easiest time when adding muscle mass, but their quests are fraught with pitfalls. Mesomorphs' metabolisms are so finely tuned and efficient that everything they eat is used. If they eat largely protein, they become muscular, but if they consume too much fat or carbohydrate, they can become quite fat.

The trick, then, is for mesomorphs to eat a high-protein diet and adjust the fat and carbohydrate levels to either maintain or reduce bodyfat levels. This involves a diet strategy that, like the bodybuilding program, is about halfway between that of ectomorphs and endomorphs.

Using a five-meal-per-day plan, here is a diet suitable for weight gain by mesomorphic bodybuilders.

Meal One (8 A.M.)
Scrambled eggs
Ham
Fruit juice or fresh fruit
Supplements

Meal Two (11 A.M.)
Tuna salad
Two pieces of fruit
Nonfat raw milk
Supplements

Meal Three (2 P.M.)
Steak
Salad
Potato dish
Iced tea (with artificial sweetener)
Supplements

Meal Four (5 P.M.)
Protein milkshake
Supplements

Meal Five (8 P.M.)
Baked chicken
Rice dish
Vegetable
Yogurt
Diet soda
Supplements

The quantities of food in this menu are still small and are about halfway between what should be eaten by endomorphs and ectomorphs. If it becomes necessary to eat after the 8 P.M. meal, make that feeding a protein food such as eggs, cheese, or cold turkey.

Nutritional Supplementation

Although the next chapter is devoted to the subject of nutrition, several specific concepts that relate directly to weight gain are discussed in detail here. It is possible to accelerate your muscle-mass production by 10 to 20 percent simply by applying them to your regimen.

Raw milk and fertile eggs, for example, have long been considered ideal weight-gaining foods. In both, the nutrients are "potentiated" compared with their counterparts, pasteurized milk and nonfertilized eggs. As I noted previously, pasteurization cancels much of the usable protein in raw milk. In the same way, hens need a rooster around to produce the best-quality eggs.

Together, milk and eggs supply protein of a high biological value. Indeed, eggs are used as the standard of comparison when determining the biological value of food protein. For this reason, I strongly suggest you use a milk-and-egg protein powder in all of your protein shakes, instead of meat-based or soy powders (both of which are inferior in biological quality).

While animal-source proteins are generally superior for weight gain, you should not neglect vegetable proteins in your everyday diet. This is particularly true if you're on a limited budget, since vegetable proteins are less expensive. It takes four pounds of grain to turn out a pound of beef, with much of the protein being metabolized for energy in the process. This causes a pound of beef to cost considerably more than four pounds of grain.

Fresh seed sprouts are superior sources of protein, and I use them on all of my salads. Some other good vegetable-protein sources are soy as well as all other types of beans, corn, all types of grass grains, and all nuts.

The primary drawback to using vegetable proteins is that they are "incomplete" (i.e., lacking in one or more of the 10 essential amino acids). Essential aminos are those that the human body can't produce by itself; they must be present, or your body can't use them. Thus, grains and the like should be eaten along with eggs, meat, milk, or some other complete protein to help "complete" the vegetable protein. A good example of such a combination is whole-grain cereal with nonfat raw milk.

Numerous food supplements other than the aforementioned protein powders can help you to gain weight at a quicker pace. However, I'm not a big booster of supplements. If you're following a balanced diet, your body really doesn't need them, but if you want to gain weight quickly, there's no disputing the point that supplements can play a role. The most important of these is the group of B-complex vitamins, which help to both stimulate your appetite and build the actual muscle tissue.

While you can get a lot of B-complex from your everyday diet, it's vital that you supplement what you eat with B-complex capsules or tablets. I'd suggest taking your B-complex vitamins along with desiccated liver, which improves training endurance and drive. Other helpful supplements include vitamin C, chelated minerals, and vitamin E. All will aid in improving your general health, and the healthier you are, the better your training will go. And the better your training and diet, the faster your rate of muscle growth.

Heavy Training

The best way to gain weight is by using heavy weights, low reps, and a moderate number of sets, as we have discussed. Repetitions in the range of four to six have been scientifically determined to result in the fastest muscle-mass gains.

Doing at least one or two sets in this rep range with absolute-limit weights will give you great gains.

Another key is to apply these heavy weights and low reps to *basic exercises*. A basic exercise is one that works more than one muscle group. *Isolation exercises*, on the other hand, work only a single muscle group or, in some cases, only a segment of that muscle.

My experience in bodybuilding has allowed me to identify the best basic exercises for each body part. My list follows.

- **Thighs:** Squats, Leg Presses
- **Back:** Bent-Over Rows, Seated Pulley Rows, Shrugs, Stiff-Legged Deadlifts
- **Chest:** Bench Presses, Incline Presses, Parallel-Bar Dips
- **Shoulders:** Military Presses, Presses Behind the Neck, Upright Rows
- **Biceps:** Barbell Curls, Dumbbell Curls
- **Triceps:** Narrow-Grip Bench Presses, Barbell Triceps Extensions
- **Forearms:** Reverse Curls
- **Calves:** Standing Calf Raises, Seated Calf Raises
- **Abdominals:** Sit-Ups, Leg Raises

Also crucial in weight-gain training, as I stressed earlier, is the length of rest intervals between sets. Remember: while using heavy weights, there is a constant temptation to take long rests between sets. I've seen bodybuilders resting as long as five minutes! Such long rests erode your muscle-gain rate and leave you open to injury. Be sure to rest no longer than one minute between sets, with the exceptions as noted in the instructions, regardless of the weights you're using. This will ensure maximum gains.

A final factor in gaining weight is to emphasize leg and back training. These are the largest muscle groups in the body, and it takes hard training to build them up, so they are often neglected. Legs and back, however, have great potential for muscle gain. Indeed, when you train them hard, there will be such a favorable influence on your metabolism that the rest of your body will grow as well.

Regardless of your somatotype or your goals, the information, diets, and training routines in this book will allow you to gain bulk and power at an amazing rate. It shouldn't be difficult to gain two to three solid pounds of body weight per month. It is also possible to gain 20 pounds on your bench press and 30 to 40 pounds on your squat each month.

How do I know how fast you can gain? Simply because I've done all of this myself. You can do it too.

12
Nutrition

When I consider that, when I first started out, I didn't have a clue about the role that proper nutrition plays in bodybuilding success, I'm sometimes amazed that I've made it as far as I have. When I was growing up, a typical breakfast in my house consisted of a glass of milk and a slice of chocolate cake. That was it! And this wasn't just an odd treat that my mother allowed me to indulge in once a month—this was my childhood breakfast! It's hard to believe, but my dad would buy a huge chocolate cake whenever he got off work—it was about four inches thick! If chocolate cake wasn't available, then it was Yankee Doodles or Ring Dings, anything that was sweet-tasting but that contained "zero" nutritional benefit.

I'm not blaming my parents for this, as they were just as ignorant about proper nutrition as I was. However, I was fortunate to learn about the cause-and-effect relationship of nutrition and physical performance from all of the books and magazines that I read on bodybuilding. For the sake of my health, I'm awfully glad that I did.

Garbage In

My first indication that something funny was going on in my body occurred one morning after I'd eaten three or four large slices of cake. After I had left for school, I felt rather odd; whereas I'd normally be reserved and conservative, I found myself hyper and agitated. Then, about two hours later, I fell asleep in class. This was the standard pattern of my mornings at school: Charge in ready to rip the roof off the building, hang out with my buddies in the hall where I'd be bouncing off the walls with energy, and then, after sitting down in class, nod off and go to sleep.

What was happening is that my insulin levels were jumping all over the board to handle the influx of sugar of which my breakfast consisted. They'd rise to meet the demand of the sugar-laden cake, and the abnormally high insulin level would also knock out some of the sugar in my blood that I needed for energy to remain alert, functional, and—most important—conscious! I didn't realize this, and certainly would not have been able to articulate it, until years later. At the time, I just thought my classes must have been exceptionally boring.

In a related incident, my father was diagnosed with Hodgkin's disease at the age of 35, and a lump formed in his neck. This was no small cause for concern in our family, as I'd lost a grandfather to Hodgkin's disease several years before. The doctor who made the initial diagnosis had told my father that he had only two years to live. This was naturally a very scary period for my dad as well as the rest of the family. Fortunately the doctor was wrong, and my father is, at age 71, one of the oldest living Hodgkin's disease patients in the world. The relevance of this story to our discussion of nutrition involves my father's approach to diet.

In the old days, it was chocolate cake for breakfast. Today, he's a fanatic about diet; there can be absolutely no preservatives in his food or anything that isn't 100 percent nutritionally sound. I believe that his 180-degree turnaround on nutrition is a large contributor to his success in battling the debilitating effects of Hodgkin's disease.

I'm sure that eating what was, in essence, garbage for breakfast and snacks actually arrested my physical development. It made me struggle unnecessarily over the years to get "cut up," or to become more defined, because I was pumping all of that sugar in my body. I hardly ate any protein at all in those days, restricting my macronutrient intake almost exclusively to carbohydrates and fats. (Macronutrients are discussed in detail later in the chapter.) I had to learn the hard way just how important protein was to building muscle and priming one's metabolism. I realized when I was working out that I was not making the gains that I should have been making, and the reason stemmed back to what I was shoveling into my mouth every morning at the breakfast table.

Nutrition Is "Everything"

Nutrition not only affects the way you look and creates the energy necessary for you to train and recover at peak efficiency, but it also strongly impacts the way you feel. Nutrition fuels the brain and, consequently, affects the way the brain functions. This means that your thought processes can be thrown askew if you don't make a point to attend to nutritional needs. On

a "zero"-fat diet, for example, you'll often feel lightheaded and dizzy. The reason? Simply that you need fat in your diet. On a "zero"-carbohydrate diet, you can expect to be confused easily and have a difficult time making simple decisions. The reason? You need carbohydrates in your diet. In fact, your brain derives 99.9 percent of its nutrition from carbohydrates.

Balance

The bottom line in all nutritional matters is to eat a well-balanced diet that comprises ample portions of all of the macronutrients: protein, carbohydrates, and fats. This applies to everyone, from construction workers and bodybuilders to schoolteachers and housewives. You have to have a balanced diet for both your body and brain to function at optimum levels. Poor nutrition robs your body of vitamins and breaks down your resistance.

Some current research suggests that vitamins, such as vitamin C, can not only cure and prevent colds but also boost your immune system. I don't believe they do any such thing, as there is no single micronutrient (which is what vitamins and minerals are) that, taken in isolation, will yield "miracle" benefits. The body has specific needs of all of the vitamins and minerals, not just some, and it obtains these from all of the foods you consume—providing that your diet is balanced.

Balancing your diet is not a difficult task. Those who say, "I don't always have time to eat a balanced diet" are copping out. Diet is a volitional matter; you choose what you put into your mouth, and you always have a choice. If your diet isn't balanced, it's because you've chosen not to make it so. To redress this, rather than spend thousands of dollars annually on supplements, simply choose the food you're going to be consuming a little more wisely.

The RDAs

A balanced diet consists of so-called ample portions of protein, carbohydrates, fats, and water, while avoiding such items as preservatives and

sauces. While you need some fats, you should keep your intake to a minimum. Current standards of a well-balanced diet derive from the Food and Nutrition Board of the National Research Council of the National Academy of Sciences, which was assigned the responsibility during the Second World War of defining the nutritional requirements for Americans (the result of which was the publication of Recommended Dietary Allowances, or RDAs as they have since become known). The Food and Nutrition Board determined that a well-balanced diet is achieved by eating "ample portions" from what they termed the "Four Food Group Plan," consisting of "Cereals and Grain Foods, Fruits and Vegetables, the High-Protein Group, and Dairy Products."

What are "ample portions"? In order for your diet to be balanced, the RDAs indicate that you should be getting four servings a day from the Cereals and Grain Foods group (which con-

sists of foods such as bread and flour products, cereals, and baked goods), at least four servings a day from the Fruits and Vegetables group, at least two servings a day from the High-Protein group (meat, eggs, poultry, fish, and certain vegetable items such as dried beans, peas, and nuts), and two servings a day from the Dairy Products group (milk and cheese).

Lest you think the RDAs are ancient and therefore have no bearing on modern nutritional reality, you should know that they are periodically reviewed and revised to keep up with advances in nutritional science. Still, if you are a hardcore bodybuilder, both your weight and activity levels will be beyond those of normal healthy individuals in the U.S., so you may need more calories, protein, and B vitamins—particularly thiamine—than the average individual. As thiamine can be found in most carbohydrate foods, however, you don't need to rush out and buy a supplement.

The Macronutrients

Now let's look at each of the three macronutrients a little more in depth.

Protein

Protein derives its name from a Greek word meaning "of first importance." True, that doesn't mean "of only importance," but it underscores the necessity of this macronutrient. Proteins are composed of oxygen, carbon, hydrogen, and nitrogen. Further, they consist of 22 basic constituent elements called amino acids, 10 of which cannot be manufactured within the body and must therefore be obtained from the foods you eat throughout the day. As I mentioned in Chapter 11, those that cannot be manufactured within the body are called "essential" amino acids.

Certain foods contain all of the amino acids necessary to produce protein that is completely usable by the body. Examples include eggs, meat, milk, and fish, along with certain vegetable products such as soybeans. All of these foods contain various quantities of usable protein in ratio to their weight. For example, an egg contains a mere 12 percent protein by weight, but, because of the quantity of amino acids present in that protein, 94 percent of it can be utilized by your body. In comparison, cheese is also high in protein, but its makeup is such that your body cannot use 30 percent of it. Thus, there is a monumental difference between the protein quantity of certain foods and the "usability" of that protein in the process of building muscle.

The following chart should help you determine the foods that provide the greatest amounts of usable protein.

Food	% Protein by Weight	% Net Protein Utilization
Meat and Fowl	19–31	68
Fish	18–25	80
Eggs	12	94
Cheese	22–36	70
Milk	4	82
Brown Rice	8	70
Soybean Flour	42	61

Protein builds muscle. However, unlike some other nutrients, it cannot be stored in your body, with the result that, to receive maximum benefits, you must consume protein in adequate quantities throughout the day. Protein also serves many other functions, such as tissue repair and growth. Plus, if you're dieting, it helps to retard your appetite, suppressing the craving for sweets and carbohydrates. Protein is also important for ligament and tendon strength, as it has all the necessary nutrients for a healthy, strong body.

The best sources of protein are fish, poultry, eggs, and meat—providing it's ground beef or flank steak, as these are the lowest in fat. I don't necessarily feel that you have to eat meat every day, but it is a great source of protein. Whole milk is also good for gaining weight. If you're concerned about the fat in whole milk, then stick with lowfat milk.

Carbohydrates

Carbohydrates are very important to proper nutrition, as they constitute the bulk of our energy source. Composed of various combinations of carbon (C) and water (H_2O), carbohydrate foods are typically classified as either simple or complex.

Simple carbohydrates are easily and quickly metabolized and converted into glucose, which is, in turn, stored in the liver and in the muscles in the form of glycogen for immediate or later use by the body. However, the simple sugars found in junk foods (such as chocolate cake) are the worst thing in the world for anybody—not

just bodybuilders—to eat. My experience with fluctuating energy levels illustrates that eating simple sugars results in a very quick wave of energy followed by an equally quick crash as insulin is secreted by the pancreas to drive the blood-sugar level back to normal.

The carbohydrate foods of choice for most bodybuilders come from complex carbohydrates, which, while metabolized more slowly by the body, provide a more steady and sustained energy release. My favorite sources of complex carbohydrates are potatoes, rice, grains, and vegetables. Occasionally, if I feel the need for some simple carbohydrates, I'll consume some fresh fruit, particularly fruit with a high water content such as melons.

Fats

Fats, the third macronutrient, are composed of the same elements as carbohydrates—namely carbon, hydrogen, and oxygen—but they differ in the way that these atoms are connected. Fats are grouped in three categories: simple or "triglycerides," compound or "phospholipids," and derived or "cholesterol." Fats serve many functions in the body, including the provision of stored energy, protection and "padding" of the internal organs, and insulation of the body from extremely cold temperatures.

Fats are the most calorie-dense of the three macronutrients, with an energy yield of 3,500 calories per pound (versus only 1,600 per pound for protein and carbohydrates). Fat molecules also differ biochemically in the way they're constituted, being either saturated, unsaturated, or polyunsaturated. Diets high in saturated fats (from foods such as butter, chocolate, beef, vegetable shortening, and cream) tend to raise the cholesterol level of blood. Therefore, most reputable nutritional scientists recommend that you obtain the bulk of your fat intake in the form of polyunsaturated fats (e.g., safflower oil, walnuts, almonds, corn oil, fish, and pecans).

I've learned over the years that when I would go on a very-low-carbohydrate, high-protein diet, my fat intake would be down to almost zero.

During this period, I would often feel weak and become dizzy, and my muscles lacked fullness. Fats will give your muscles fullness. People who try to completely eliminate fat from their diets end up with very unbalanced diets—the exact opposite of what they should be striving for. Fat is very important.

Water

One of the most overlooked elements of a well-balanced diet is water. This fluid is vital to the transport of various chemicals throughout the system and also is the medium though which the various biochemical reactions that lead to energy transference take place. The body itself is 70 percent water, as are our muscles.

I consume two gallons of water every day—but then I'm 6'5" and 300 pounds. For the average person, I would recommend drinking four or five eight-ounce glasses a day, or three-quarters of a gallon. This doesn't mean that you should drink this amount at one time. Instead, consume water throughout the course of the day. Water is essential for losing weight; it washes out the impurities from your body and plays a major role in maintaining your health.

The Micronutrients

Micronutrients, so called because they are required in very small quantities on a daily basis, can be obtained from eating a well-balanced diet consisting of adequate servings from the aforementioned macronutrients. Following is a breakdown of all of the micronutrients—vitamins and minerals—your body needs to operate at maximum efficiency.

Vitamins

- **A:** Crucial for growth and repair of tissues and also important for eyesight. Fights bacteria and infection, and aids in the formation of bones and teeth.
- **B Complex:** Vital for the metabolism of carbohydrates, proteins, and fats by the body. Assists in the healthy functioning of the nervous system and maintains muscle tone in the gastrointestinal tract. Also helps maintain hair, skin, eyes, and liver.
- **B_1 (Thiamine):** Serves to metabolize carbohydrates, maintains health of the nervous system, and retards appetite. Also assists in muscle growth.
- **B_2 (Riboflavin):** Necessary for metabolism of all the macronutrients; aids in the formation of antibodies and red blood cells.
- **B_6 (Pyridoxine):** Required for macronutrient metabolism, aids in the formation of antibodies, and helps maintain the body's balance of sodium and phosphorus.
- **B_{12} (Cyanocobalamin):** Crucial for the formulation of blood cells and the metabolism of all macronutrients. Apart from this, B_{12} is also a requisite in keeping your nervous system fully functional.
- **B_{13} (Orotic Acid):** Required primarily for the optimal metabolism of some B vitamins.
- **Bioflavinoids:** Helps in increasing the structural integrity of capillaries.
- **Biotin:** Necessary for macronutrient metabolism as well as metabolism of B vitamins.
- **C:** Maintains collagen and helps to repair wounds, fractures, and scar tissue. Also imparts strength to blood vessels. Vitamin C aids in resistance to infection and in absorption of iron as well.
- **Choline:** Plays an important role as a regulator of nerve transmission while aiding in metabolizing fats and regulating the liver and gallbladder.
- **D:** Improves absorption and utilization of calcium and phosphorus required for proper bone formation. Further serves to maintain a stable nervous system and normal heart function.
- **E:** Protects fat-soluble vitamins and red blood cells and is essential for cellular respiration. Vitamin E also inhibits the coagulation of blood by preventing clotting.

- **F:** Important for vital respiration of organs. Helps to maintain the resilience and fabrication of cells while regulating blood circulation and normal glandular activity.
- **Folic Acid:** Critical for proper respiration of organs. Helps maintain resilience and fabrication of cells while regulating blood circulation and normal glandular activity.
- **Inositol:** Vital for the formation of lecithin and hair growth. Indirectly connected to the metabolism of fats, including cholesterol.
- **K:** Required for the formulation of prothrombin, a protein required for proper blood coagulation.
- **Laetrile (B$_{17}$):** Has been linked to cancer prevention.
- **Niacin:** Necessary for macronutrient metabolism; maintains health of skin, tongue, and digestive system.
- **PABA:** Aids bacteria in producing folic acid. Acts as a coenzyme in the breakdown and utilization of proteins and aids in the formation of red blood cells.
- **Pangamic Acid (B$_{15}$):** Helps eliminate hypoxia (a deficiency of oxygen reaching the body's tissues) and promotes protein metabolism and stimulation of the nervous and glandular systems.
- **Pantothenic Acid:** Participates in the release of energy from carbohydrates, fats, and proteins while aiding in the utilization of some vitamins. Also improves the body's resistance to stress.

Minerals
- **Calcium:** Necessary for the development and maintenance of strong teeth and bones. Further assists in normal blood clotting and nerve and heart function.
- **Chlorine:** Serves to regulate acid-base balance, maintains osmotic pressure while stimulating production of hydrochloric acid, and helps maintain joints and tendons.
- **Chromium:** Stimulates enzymes in the metabolism of energy and the synthesis of fatty acids, cholesterol, and protein. Also increases the effectiveness of insulin.
- **Cobalt:** Functions as part of vitamin B$_{12}$ and maintains red blood cells while activating many enzymes.
- **Copper:** Serves in the formation of red blood cells. Works in conjunction with vitamin C to form elastin.
- **Fluorine:** May reduce tooth decay by discouraging the growth of acid-forming bacteria.
- **Iodine:** An essential part of the hormone thyroxin. Necessary in the prevention of goiter and further serves to regulate the production of energy and the rate of metabolism. Also promotes growth.
- **Iron:** Serves in the formation of hemoglobin and myoglobin, and promotes protein metabolism and growth.
- **Magnesium:** Acts as a catalyst in the utilization of macronutrients as well as the micronutrients calcium, phosphorus, and possibly potassium.
- **Manganese:** An enzyme activator, playing a part in the production of carbohydrates and fats. Also necessary for proper skeletal development and maintaining sex-hormone production.
- **Molybdenum:** Serves in the oxidation of fats and aldehydes. Also aids in mobilization of iron from the reserves of the liver.
- **Nickel:** Known to activate several enzyme systems; also present in ribonucleic acids (RNA).
- **Phosphorus:** Works with calcium to build bones and teeth. Helps to utilize carbohydrates, fats, and proteins. Also serves as a catalyst in muscle contraction.
- **Potassium:** Serves to control the activity of heart muscle, the nervous system, and the kidneys.
- **Selenium:** Works with vitamin C. Preserves tissue elasticity.
- **Sodium:** Maintains normal fluid levels in cell tissue. Also maintains the health of the nervous, blood, lymph, and muscular systems.

- **Sulfur:** Part of amino acids and B vitamins. Necessary for tissue formation and collagen synthesis.
- **Vanadium:** Inhibits cholesterol formation.
- **Zinc:** Component of insulin and male reproductive fluid. Aids in the digestion and metabolism of phosphorus and is very helpful in healing.

Meal Spacing

The secret to gaining weight (apart from the training, of course) is to eat small quantities of food four to six times per day, as opposed to the more prevalent two to three large meals each day. Protein builds muscle tissue, it's true, but your body can digest and use only 30–40 grams of protein per feeding. Because of this, it definitely makes sense to eat smaller meals more frequently.

I'd recommend that you eat one to one-and-a-half grams of protein per pound of body weight daily. As listed earlier, the best protein sources are fish, fowl, beef, eggs, and milk products. Beans, peas, and grains are also good protein sources, but vegetable proteins lack one or two of the essential amino acids, so you'll have to combine these foods with other vegetable- or animal-protein sources to complete the amino-acid balance.

You should consume a balanced diet to go with your protein, of course. Concentrate on fresh fruits and vegetables, including potatoes, green salads, nuts, seeds, and grains. I'd also suggest that you take one or two multivitamin/mineral supplements daily as insurance against progress-halting nutritional deficiencies.

If you're unsure what to eat specifically, here's a sample nutritional schedule for one day that I highly recommend.

Meal One (8 A.M.)
Cheese omelet with 4–5 eggs
Whole-grain toast
1 piece of fruit
1–2 glasses of whole milk

Meal Two (11 A.M.)
2 meat or cheese sandwiches on whole-grain bread
3 ounces of raw nuts
1–2 glasses of whole milk

Meal Three (2 P.M.)
Tuna salad
Piece of fresh fruit sliced on yogurt
1–2 glasses of whole milk

Meal Four (5 P.M.)
1 protein drink (consisting of 1 pint of whole milk, ⅓ cup of milk-and-egg protein powder, and fruit or another flavoring for taste)
This should be your pre-workout meal, since it will give you an abundance of protein and training energy.

Meal Five (8 P.M.)
Steak
Vegetable
Baked potato
1–2 glasses of whole milk

Meal Six (11 P.M.)
3 ounces of hard cheese
3 ounces of raw sunflower seeds
1–2 glasses of whole milk
As an alternative, you can have another protein drink.

The pre-bedtime meal is essential, since the calories and protein in this last meal aren't needed for normal daily activity and tissue repair. As a result, the nutrients in this meal are more readily available to build tissue while you sleep. You actually build the most muscle while sleeping!

Milk has long been touted as a weight-gain food, and whole milk is wonderful for this purpose. However, as I pointed out in Chapter 11, some bodybuilders are allergic to the lactose (sugar) in milk. Since hard cheeses don't have lactose, you can simply increase your cheese intake to get the same effect as drinking two to three quarts of milk per day.

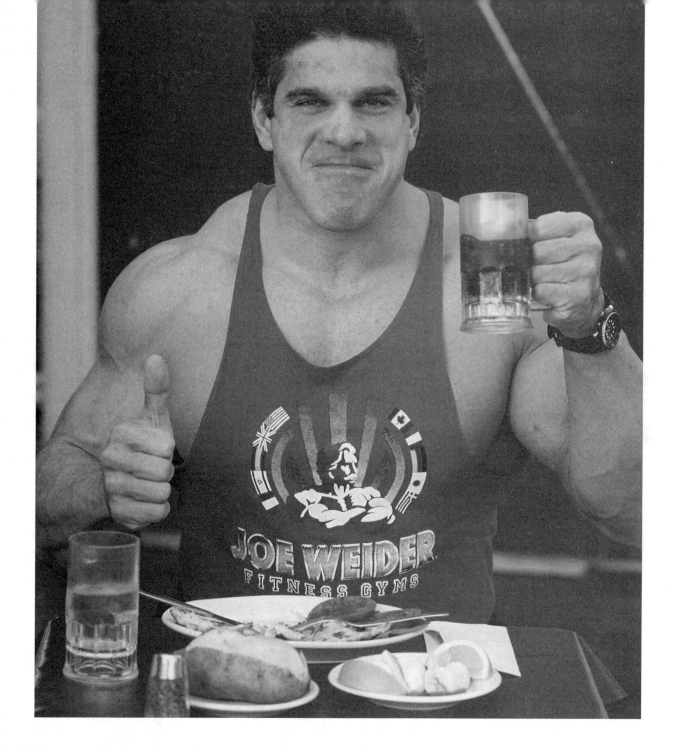

No matter your personal goal (whether to lose weight or to gain), you must keep your diet balanced. You can't go on a starvation or crash diet because, if you starve your body and deny it one of the macronutrients, as soon as you go off your diet, you'll binge like a lunatic and gain more weight than before.

Losing Fat

If you're dieting to lose body fat, be aware right off the bat that trying to accomplish too much too soon can lead to terrible physique problems. The human body takes its time adapting to certain physiological states, and change is welcome (if at all) only in bits. For this reason, it's always a mistake to cut your calories to an extreme low or to dramatically increase your work output. The body prefers to keep things the same, a state that physiologists refer to as homeostasis. No matter how badly you want to lose fat, you can't buck this reality.

Fortunately, you can learn to work with homeostasis to achieve your desired results. For instance, when I begin preparing for a contest, I'll start with very mild aerobic activity. After a couple of weeks of, say, 20-minute sessions two or three times a week, I'll slowly increase the duration, at which point my real aerobic program begins. In order to lose fat successfully, I know that I'll need to start my aerobics at a 30-minute every-other-day pace. I'll typically begin by performing a half-hour on one of three pieces of equipment: the stationary bike, the treadmill, or the stairclimber.

I'll gradually begin to phase in my aerobic activity to an every-day pace, including the "rest" days of my training schedule. This is accomplished by increasing my aerobic activity by 30-minute increments. I'll tack an additional 15 minutes onto my first aerobic session of the day to increase it to 45 minutes straight (usually on the treadmill). When I return to the gym in the evening, I'll train another body part and knock off another 45 minutes straight on either the treadmill or the stationary bike. Such a process is gradual enough to not cause my body to panic and yet progressive enough to begin to melt the fat.

At this stage, I like to perform my aerobic work every day. Even on "off" days, I feel the need to keep my cardiovascular system in high gear. I'll do an average of one-and-a-half hours of cardio a day—not all at once, but in the format I've just outlined.

After two weeks or so on this program, I'll again increase my cardio work by adding five minutes to each session, so that I'm now performing 25 minutes per apparatus for a total of 50 minutes per session. Again, this isn't done right out of the gate, which would result in over-

training. I allow my body one to two weeks at each level. That way, it gets used to the increased aerobic workload, so the change is perceived as gradual rather than severe.

I'll continue in this mode (i.e., 90 to 100 minutes of aerobic activity per day) up until one week out from the contest, at which point I'll make some more minor modifications. These adjustments come in the form of trading an aerobic session for a daily bout of isometric posing to practice both my muscle control and my ability to sustain a given pose for a prolonged period. This latter factor is crucial for a competitive bodybuilder.

For becoming more muscular, I'm a strong believer in a moderate- to high-protein diet. For me, that means chicken, egg whites, and red meat. I'll go from eating red meat once or twice a day to once a day the last six weeks out from the show, but I'll continue to eat lots of chicken.

I'll often combine my egg whites with chicken breasts, tuna, or turkey and will consciously cut back a bit on my carbs and increase my protein intake as well. Why? Simply because I don't want to drop a lot of weight too quickly, nor do I want my body to burn muscle. Just as you should do with aerobics, you must give your body time to adapt and adjust to what you're doing and not panic it into a fat-storage mode.

I'll give my body the protein-rich food it requires to maintain my condition and continue to build muscle mass as I keep dropping weight throughout the aerobic sessions. I'll also eat more vegetables, such as broccoli, corn, peas, beans, and salads with vinegar-and-oil dressing (or lemon juice), as these are the kinds of foods that best replace carbs. Instead of rice, for example, I'll have some of these vegetables. While I still get some carbs from them, they're lower in calories and also serve to fill me up so that I don't get as hungry or uncomfortable. When I want to get harder still, I'll drop my carb intake just a bit more and also increase my aerobics slightly.

It's also at this point that I implement my multivitamin/mineral supplements. Because of my reduced food intake, these become even more important, since I'm training very hard, performing more aerobics, and tanning, which causes me to sweat out even more valuable vitamins and minerals.

Cutting Calories

Even though I cut my calories considerably before a contest, I don't generally suffer any ill effects from my diet. Many bodybuilders tell me that they feel weak and somewhat listless as a result of cutting back two or three weeks out from a show. I'm not saying that this has never happened to me, but normally it doesn't occur until a week or so out. At that time, I'll implement a three-days-low/two-days-high system of caloric allotment. I can't tell you how low my calories actually drop, but if my physique continues to improve each day, I know they're low enough, and if I start to flatten out, I'll simply increase my calories (in the form of carbs) slightly to remedy it. I let the mirror, not the scale, dictate whether I need to decrease or increase my caloric intake.

I know that many people count their calories like scientists, but if I had to be that intense about it, bodybuilding would be much more work than it actually is for me. I prefer just looking in the mirror. It tells me whether I'm fat or whether I'm drained and need more carbs.

Here's a typical pre-contest meal breakdown for the average bodybuilder looking to lose fat. I'd recommend that people following such a diet stay with it until one or two weeks out, at which point I would substitute fish for some of the poultry.

8 A.M.
10 egg whites
Medium bowl of oatmeal with a handful of raisins
8–12 ounces of water
1 multivitamin/mineral tablet

11:15 A.M.
1 chicken breast
1 big bowl of brown rice
1 fruit platter (mainly melons and bananas)
Half a tuna sandwich on whole-wheat bread

2:30 P.M.
2 chicken breasts
Medium-size bowl of brown and white rice (mixed)

5 P.M.
1 chicken breast mixed in with 6 egg whites cooked with a nonfat cooking spray on a bed of rice
1 multivitamin/mineral supplement
1 glass of water

8:30 P.M.
1 6–8 ounce turkey breast cut into strips and mixed in with 6 egg whites, onions, and bell peppers
Large helping of mixed vegetables
Water

I have found this to be the perfect system of combining aerobics and dieting to really lose body fat while also keeping my sanity intact. Give this gradual-progression system a shot and see if it doesn't do the same for you. Remember, it takes time to reach your goals. Most people like to go on diets for periods of six to eight weeks—sorry, it doesn't work like that. Balanced nutrition takes months of consistency. It's actually a year-round endeavor, and once you get into the correct mode of eating, your body's metabolism will be in high gear, your body fat will be low, and most important, you'll be operating at 100 percent peak efficiency.

13
My *Hercules* Training Log

Ever since I filmed the movie *Hercules*, in 1982, bodybuilding fans have asked how I trained in order to have gotten into such tight shape. While I can't point to a single "magic" routine, I can provide several routines that, when combined, resulted in the overall appearance I displayed in the movie.

People find it hard to believe that the peak physical condition I achieved was obtained with very little equipment. We were in Italy, and all I had on the site was an Olympic barbell set, a bench, and a pair of dumbbells. During the early stages of filming, I did no squats at all and trained almost exclusively using the superset principle (in which you do two exercises in a row without resting in between sets). I remember stripping the weights off of one end of the Olympic set, jamming the weightless end into the corner of the room I was using for training,

loading up the other end of the barbell, and then performing makeshift T-bar rows with it!

As strange as it may seem, the workouts I had on the set of *Hercules* were among the most productive of my entire career. I was focused, I had good concentration, and the equipment was sparse enough that I knew I had to make the most out of what was before me, rather than looking around for a "better" piece of apparatus.

Later on in the filming, I was able to locate a gym that had a Smith machine, a Roman Chair, and a complete Universal gym, which afforded me a little more variety—but I still think back on those earlier spartan workouts with a certain fondness.

What follows are the actual weight-training programs, along with my personal pointers, reminders, and daily scheduling that put me in what some people have considered to be my all-time best shape.

Workouts for Location

Shoulders   Hercules

Laterals
Barbell Press Behind Neck   } 8 sets

Upright Barbell Row
Bent over Laterals   } 6 sets

Biceps

Alternate Dumbell Curl - 6 sets

Barbell Curl
E-Z Bar Curls   } 6 sets

Tricers   Forearms Reverse Curls / Wrist

Lying French Press Decline   16 - 18 sets

Standing French Press

Abdominals

Incline Leg Raises   15 - 20 sets
Crunches
Decline Situps

WORKOUT FOR LOCATION
HERCULES 1

Chest

DUMBELL PRESSES INCLINE
INCLINE BARBELL PRESS } 7 SETS

DECLINE FLYES
VERY WIDE GRIP FLAT
BENCH PRESSES } 6 SETS

DUMBELL PULLOVERS - 6 SETS

BACK

BARBELL ROWS 8-10 SETS - VARIATION
OF GRIP

T-BAR ROWING
ONE ARM DUMBELL ROW } 6-8 SETS

DEADLIFTS - BENT LEGGED DEADLIFTS - 4-6

THIGHS

HALF SQUATS - 6 SETS - 15-20 REPS
LUNGES - 4-6 SETS - 10-15 REPS

<u>My Typical Film Schedule</u>

- 1) Arise at 5:00 AM
- 2) Leave Hotel at 5:30 AM with Cab
- 3) Snack Bar → Coffee 5:50 AM
- 4) 6 AM → Set up Equipment for Workout
- 5) 6:15 AM → Begin Training
- 6) 8:35 → Finish Workout
- 7) 8:45-9 AM → Shower and Clean up
- 8) 9 AM — 9:15 → Breakfast at Bar
- 9) 9:30 → Leave for Location
- 10) 10 AM → Arrive at Location
- 11) 10:15 → Make up and Costume
- 12) 10:30 → Begin Shooting - Rehearsals
- 13) 1 PM → Break for Lunch
- 14) 2 PM → Finish Lunch and Makeup
- 15) 2:15 PM → Start Shooting
- 16) 7:30 - 8 PM → Finish Shooting
- 17) 8:15 PM → Leave - Return to Hotel
- 18) 8:45 — 9M → Arrive at Hilton Hotel -
       Depending on Rush Hour
- 19) 9:15 → Eat Dinner - Room or Resturant -
       Downstairs in Lobby
- 20) 9:45 → Finish Dinner
- 21) 9:45 - 10 PM → Organize Gym Bag, Vitamins,
       Fruit and Materials to Take
- 22) 10:20 → — Relax till Tired
- 23) 11:30 PM — Midnight → Retire

This has been my schedule - six days - week -
                              five months - no vac.

TIPS TO REMEMBER FOR MAXIMUM DEFINITON DURING TRAINING

1) REALLY BEGIN WITH PRE-PLANNED PROGRAM AND WORKING WITH THE MIND TO KEEP A STRONG POSITIVE ENTHUSIASM REGARDLESS WHATEVER HAPPENS PRIOR TO TRAINING TIME

2) KNOW ROUTINE + VARIOUS EXERCISES BEFORE BEGINNING

3) FEEL AND USE STRICTEST FORM ON EVERY REPETITION EVEN THOUGH YOU ARE WARMING UP

4) MOVE GRACEFULLY, NOT RUSHING OR BANGING INTO EQUIPMENT

5) IF TIME IS SHORT, THEN DO THE EXERCISES YOU THINK ARE MOST VITAL

6) USE REST TIME BETWEEN SETS TO ORGANIZE APPARATUS FOR NEXT BODYPART. KEEP OCCUPIED

7) PRACTICE POSING ALSO IN BETWEEN TO CHECK ON PROGRESS

8) REMEMBER - YOU WILL OBTAIN 100% IF YOU DO YOUR HOMEWORK NIGHT BEFORE

9) ORGANIZE YOUR GYM CLOTHES, BAG + TOWELS NIGHT BEFORE. YOU NEED A FREE CLEAR HEAD ESPECIALLY EARLY MORNING

10) HAVE COFFEE AND ONLY 1 PIECE OF FRUIT - SO YOU WON'T FEEL SLUGGISH OR NAUSEATED

FRIDAY'S WORKOUT – IF TIRED

GIANT SET – CYCLE

1) SQUAT (SMITH MACH)
2) INCLINE SITUPS (45°)
3) STANDING TOE RAISES
4) SISSY SQUATS
5) ROMAN CHAIR SITUPS
6) UNIVERSAL MACH. TOE RAISES
7) LEG RAISES – 20°
8) ROPE PULLS – 15-20 R

} 5-6 GIANT SETS

NOTE: DO GIANT SET NON-STOP W/ GOOD RHYTHM, FORM AND TECHNIQUE. GIVE 110% EFFORT AND GO TO FAILURE AT END OF EACH SET.

REMEMBER: GO ALL OUT FOR SUNDAY AND TRAINING LIKE OUTLINED WILL ENHANCE YOUR DEFINITION TREMENDOUSLY.

OR DO GIANT SETS IN TWO PHASES AS DESCRIBED ON OTHER SHEET

14
Specialization: Shoulders

Deltoid development is surprisingly complicated. It's not so much that the training is very technical, but rather the construction of the muscle group can lead one to train incorrectly if a few basics are neglected.

The deltoid muscle is actually a three-headed group that, when well developed, will cap the sides of the shoulders. However, you have to guard against overdevelopment of the front (or anterior) deltoids. Many times I'll see overdevelopment of the front delts because of too much chest work compounded by specialized front-deltoid work. This look gives the appearance of "round" shoulders. It isn't just the case of more development of the other two heads to balance things out either, as the front-deltoid heads have the unfortunate ability to get easily overdeveloped and therefore out of proportion to the rear and lateral (or medial) heads.

The rear deltoids, on the other hand, have the opposite problem; it's almost impossible to do too much work for them. For most of us, the rear deltoids are always lagging and require special work and concentration. When the rear deltoids are really well developed, they add a whole different dimension to upper-body contour and thickness.

The lateral heads of the deltoids are the most important of the three parts of each deltoid cap. They are what gives the look of width to your upper body—from both the front and the back.

Now that I've laid out the problem for you, it's up to you to create your own individual programs based on your particular needs. I will describe all of my favorite deltoid movements and their executions, followed by several suggested routines, but the rest is up to you.

If you are a beginner, concentrate on the basic movements. It will not be until you reach the intermediate stage that you will be looking critically for flaws. The advanced stage is reserved for the detail work, the seeking out of your own personal perfection.

Deltoid Exercises

Presses Behind the Neck

My favorite deltoid movement is the press behind the neck. This movement works the whole shoulder group, with special emphasis on the lateral heads.

This is the most productive of the shoulder movements, but unfortunately, it's also one of

the most dangerous. I make this warning not to scare you off but to urge you to train intelligently and make haste "slowly," on this one especially. I always do the movement seated, but it can also be done standing. I have found that the seated version is better for me because it allows me to better isolate the shoulders without having to worry about keeping my back flat.

I start the movement with the bar pressed to arms' length overhead. I perform the movement seated on a special bench that gives me full support and is specially designed for this exercise; however, any flat bench can be used. I usually have a training partner to help me with the starting position. My feet are flat on the floor, and my back is pressed against the upright part of the bench. If you're using a flat bench instead, you should be very secure in an upright position with little or no arch to your back. It may be helpful for your training partner to stabilize your back by placing a knee against the middle.

Your grip on the bar will be one of medium width. Your upper arms should be perpendicular to your forearms at the midpoint of the movement if your grip is correct. If your grip is any narrower than this, the movement becomes very constricted, with much more triceps work and less deltoid work. Should you attempt to go any wider, you may encounter shoulder and wrist (and sometimes elbow) problems from this unnatural angle. So, the width of the grip is very important.

When I lower the weight, I just barely touch the base of my neck and then begin to press the weight back up smoothly. I've seen people try to bounce the weight out of the bottom position, and this can be disastrous. If you can't control the weight or complete the rep without dangerous contortions, the weight is simply too heavy for you. Never sacrifice style for heavier weight. It's the weight plus the movement, correctly performed, that creates the desired results.

I never completely lock out my elbows on each repetition. Instead, I keep a constant tension. I like the feel of the movement that way. As I said earlier, this movement can be dangerous, so I always start my first set with a weight with which I can easily do 15 repetitions. The danger lies in a cold, stiff shoulder joint. Warm them up properly and you should not have any problems with chronic shoulder difficulties. To ensure safety, I'd advise warming up with just the bar for two sets of 15 to 20 reps before adding weight.

Side Lateral Raises

The side lateral raise is the isolation movement for the lateral heads of the deltoids. When the movement is correctly performed, you'll be able to see and feel this isolation. My upper arms are bent slightly forward at the beginning to allow me to get the dumbbells together. I then attempt

to hold this bent-arm position throughout the movement. By keeping my torso a little bit forward rather than allowing it to lean back, I better isolate the lateral heads of my deltoids. To further emphasize the lateral portions, I will begin to rotate my hands slightly. At this point, my hands are no longer parallel to the floor, and I am beginning to lead with my little fingers while my thumbs are pointing down slightly.

The movement is not unlike pouring water out of a pitcher—it's all in the wrists. The arms stay in a slightly unlocked position throughout. This unlocking of the arms at the elbows allows for more work on the delts and less stress on the elbows. The key is to maintain the same slightly unlocked position throughout the entire movement.

At the top of the movement, because I have twisted my hands and am leaning slightly forward, the highest point that I can raise the dumbbells is to ear level. At this point, the muscle is fully contracted and can actually cramp if the position is held for more than a second or two. I'll then lower the weights slowly to the starting position and repeat. I usually do 8 to 12 reps per set of this exercise. The side lateral dumbbell raise can also be performed with one arm at a time.

One-Arm Cable Laterals

A variation on the dumbbell lateral raise that I sometimes use is the one-arm cable lateral. While it works the same area as the dumbbell lateral, the "feel" of the movement is completely different. Because the pulley keeps the tension or effective resistance the same throughout the movement, the exercise is much harder to perform at the beginning than it is with a dumbbell. This change of stress point is an important factor in achieving complete development and also adds variety to the shoulder routine. I work with one pulley at a time because it allows for more complete focus on the lateral heads of the deltoids. I usually use this movement prior to competing in a contest because it is so good at getting deep into the muscle. I start with my right hand across my left thigh. I lean slightly forward to better isolate my deltoid and then slowly bring the handle across my body while simultaneously twisting my wrist to make the movement even more effective. At the top of the movement, my hand is at ear level. Constant tension plus the wrist twist gives this movement a very good feeling and excellent results. Remember to perform the exercise in the same manner with both arms.

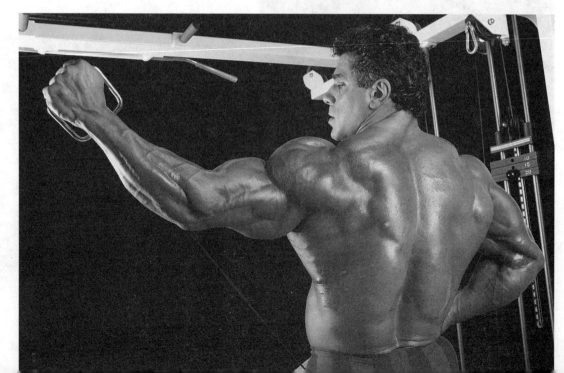

Dumbbell Presses

The dumbbell press has many of the good features of the press behind the neck with fewer of the dangers. However, you will not be able to handle as much weight. I usually start the movement while seated on a flat bench with the dumbbells facing each other. If you decide to do the exercise standing (as I sometimes do), be sure you are very upright with little or no back bend. You are working your shoulders, after all, and not your lower back. As I approach the midpoint of the movement, my hands have moved away from my body to a point where the width between the dumbbells is about the same as my grip would be on the press behind the neck. My forearms are perpendicular to the floor when my upper arms are parallel to it.

So far, the dumbbells have traveled in an arc. Just after this midpoint, I begin to rotate my hands so that the dumbbells are almost in line at the finish of the movement. The twist in the last half of the movement tends to intensify the contraction. Lower the weight slowly, and repeat. I usually use 8 to 12 reps per set.

Bent-Over Laterals

The almost-always underdeveloped rear deltoids need special attention and deep concentration if you are to produce balanced shoulder development. My favorite rear-delt movement is the bent-over lateral raise using a floor pulley. The continuous-tension aspect of all pulley work

is very much evident here, with a deep muscle burn on the last few reps of each well-executed set. I start the exercise with my feet about 18" to 24" wider than shoulder width and my back parallel to the floor. The adjustable pulley is as low to the floor as possible. This low pulley angle is essential to getting a complete contraction at the top position.

My arms are slightly unlocked at the elbows to reduce stress at this joint. As you go from this fully stretched position to the contracted position, try to keep the back flat and with a very minimum of movement to the upper body. You are attempting to isolate the rear deltoids, and that is best accomplished by reducing or eliminating all extraneous movement. The bend in the elbows should stay the same throughout the movement as well. Many times, I see this very fine rear-deltoid movement degenerate into a sloppy triceps movement by too much flexing at the elbows.

Another common error is letting the elbows fall backwards. The pulley handles should move in a straight line. If you let the elbows fall out of the straight line, you'll be giving much less work to the rear delts. This form of the "cheat" is easy to fall into because you are stronger if you let those elbows drop. Unfortunately, this added strength comes from the back muscles, which are stronger than the relatively small rear delts. You won't be able to handle a lot of weight here, but the weight is secondary to development.

Bent-Over Laterals (Dumbbell)

The dumbbell version of the bent-over lateral raise is also very effective. The same foot spacing is important because you can't get the most out of the exercise without a solid base.

I start this movement with the dumbbells facing each other and with my elbows slightly unlocked. Throughout the entire exercise, my basic position of keeping my back flat and parallel to the floor is maintained. In the early reps of each set, I attempt to hold the contracted posi-

tion for a split-second. I'll also rotate my hands slightly by lifting my little fingers as high as possible.

This rotation helps to isolate the rear delts and to enhance the productivity of the exercise. The dumbbell version of this exercise gives very little stress to the rear delts at the beginning of the movement, but the stress reaches its maximum at the end or fully contracted position. This is in contrast to the pulley version, which is very intense in the beginning third and less so in the last two-thirds.

I usually use a little back movement on the last few reps of a set to achieve full contraction. This is just a little "cheat" to help me continue through a set, but I won't cheat throughout the entire set. This type of cheat adds to the effectiveness of the movement because it allows me to get a few extra reps that I would be unable to accomplish in any other way. However, don't ever cheat by letting your elbows fall backward, as this would be counterproductive to maximum rear-delt development. Always raise those dumbbells in a straight line.

Alternate Front Dumbbell Raises

The front deltoids are almost completely isolated by the alternate front dumbbell raise. I start this movement with the dumbbells held together and almost touching in front of me. My feet are just a little wider than shoulder width. As I raise a dumbbell, I concentrate on the working delt in an attempt to isolate the front deltoid. This isolation is important so that the front delts stand as separate entities when posed. I usually limit my specific front-delt work to pre-competition, however, as I tend to get enough front-delt work out of the rest of my shoulder and chest training. At the top position, I'll again twist my hand slightly to intensify the contraction. I use a smooth, rhythmic motion and don't lean back during the movement, as I prefer to keep a slight forward bend to my upper body to further isolate the front delts.

Shoulder Routines

Novice Routine

First Month—Presses Behind the Neck: 1 set of 15 reps, 1 set of 10 reps.

Second Month—Presses Behind the Neck: 1 set of 15 reps, 1 set of 10 reps, 1 set of 8 reps. Add weight with each set.

Third Through Sixth Month—Presses Behind the Neck: 5 sets of 15/12/8/8/6 reps respectively. Add weight with each set.

Intermediate Routine

(Seventh through twelfth month)

Dumbbell Presses: 4 sets of 12/10/8/6 reps. Add weight with each set.

Dumbbell Rear Laterals: 4 sets of 12/10/8/6 reps. Add weight with each set.

Advanced Intermediate Routine

(After at least one year of serious training)

Pressing Movement: Any from this chapter, 4 sets of 15/12/8/6 reps. I vary my routine from workout to workout by choosing a different movement.

Lateral Raises: Pulley or dumbbell, 4 sets of 12/10/8/6 reps.

Rear-Delt Raises: Any variation, 4 sets of 12/10/8/8 reps.

I use this type of routine in the offseason and at times when I want to add size to my deltoids.

Advanced Routine

(For specialization and pre-contest training)

If you are specializing, cut down on the rest of your workout until your shoulders come up to par.

Pressing Movement: 4 sets of 15/12/8/6 reps.
Lateral Movement: 4 sets of 12/10/8/8 reps.
Rear-Delt Movement: 4 sets of 12/10/8/8 reps.
Front-Delt Movement: 4 sets of 12/10/8/8 reps.

Advanced Mass-Building Routine

Pressing Movement: 4 sets of 15/12/8/6 reps.
Lateral Movement: 4 sets of 15/12/8/6 reps.
Another Pressing Movement: 4 sets of 15/12/8/6 reps.
Front- or Rear-Delt Movement: 4 sets of 12/10/8/8 reps.

It's a good idea to change your exercises frequently. This applies not only to deltoids but also to every other body part you train when in the advanced stage. A constant change of angle or apparatus allows you to hit a muscle from a variety of positions, thereby stressing various fibers more severely than others. The end result is more complete and balanced development. If you are underdeveloped in the rear delts and overdeveloped in the front delts, perform two rear-delt movements and delete the front-delt movement from your routine until you're more perfectly balanced.

15
Specialization: Chest

When I'm gunning for improvement (which is every workout, by the way), there's nothing "usual" about any aspect of my training. And this is particularly evident whenever I'm training my chest.

I've always adhered to the method whereby, if I pick four or five exercises for my chest one day, I'll be sure to pick four or five different exercises the next time that I train chest. The variety allows me to hit my chest from different angles every workout, which provides for much fuller, balanced development and continued growth stimulation, as the body is never sure what's going to hit it next.

This "instinctive" philosophy also spills over to how I group my body parts together on a three- or four-day split. Pre-contest, I like to train my chest together with my back on day one, my legs alone on day two, and shoulders and arms on day three. But on any other given day, you might find me training my chest and triceps together, back with biceps, and then shoulders and legs together, so all of my workouts—every aspect of them, in fact—have a tendency to change.

My Training Split Pre-contest (3-on, 1-off split)	
Day	**Body Parts**
1	Chest, back
2	Legs
3	Delts, biceps, triceps
4	Off

Alternate Schedule (3-on, 1-off split)	
Day	**Body Parts**
1	Chest, triceps
2	Back, biceps
3	Shoulders, legs
4	Off

Given that my training is so instinctive, I can't really provide a structured program or schedule that I religiously follow all year long or that, taken in isolation, will guarantee you pec development like mine. However, I can tell you what I'm doing at this juncture of my training.

Whenever I'm gunning for additional mass on my chest, particularly in my upper-pec area, I'll start my workouts with some form of incline press, usually with a barbell. (Instructions for performing the incline barbell press and other chest exercises are included at the end of the chapter.) I'll typically perform reps of eight per set and sets of five, two of which are warm-ups.

For every exercise, I make it a point to perform three solid progressively heavier sets after my two warm-ups. Sometimes they're so heavy I need a spotter on them. Usually the only time I use a spotter is on pressing exercises.

As a rule of thumb, I normally don't go over 365 pounds on incline presses, and 315 is about my workout weight. Some people may think those are impressive numbers, but they're really not. I've lifted far heavier in the past, but for what I'm training for, they do the job just fine.

Train Like a Bodybuilder

I'm a bodybuilder, not a powerlifter, so there's not really much point in my trying to knock off singles with 415 or 500 pounds. I push myself to a weight that I can do for six or seven good, hard reps, and then I might have a partner assist me on the eighth or ninth repetition.

To recap, on my inclines, I do five total sets, two of which are warm-ups, for between 8 and 10 repetitions per set; sometimes I'll use a spotter. From there, I'll switch to a flying movement. I always try to throw a flying movement in between two pressing movements. It's great for a warm-up and an overall stretching of the muscle, and if I were to do two presses in succession, by the time I get to the flying movement I wouldn't have the same kind of strength.

Because I like to have the same-quality strength on my flyes as I do for my presses, I have to change the order of my exercises routinely. If I'm doing incline barbell presses, then flat flyes, and then flat-bench dumbbell presses, it stands to reason that my flat-bench presses are always going to suffer in terms of maximum poundages due to their placement in the routine. To obviate that, the next time I train chest, I'll do flat-bench barbell presses, incline dumbbell flyes, and then maybe incline dumbbell presses. This is what I mean by being instinctive and using a lot of variety. But again, it's still three exercises. (My pec routine is outlined in the table that follows.)

From the inclines, I go to flat flyes, using the same principle: five sets, two of which are warm-ups. I'll usually work up to 75- or 80-pound dumbbells for eight repetitions. Then I'll go into my flat-bench dumbbell presses. Another thing you may have noticed, if one pressing exercise is performed with a barbell, the next pressing exercise I do will be performed with dumbbells. I'll use one barbell press and one dumbbell press. In this example, I'll use dumbbells for my flat-bench presses, usually working up to 130-pound dumbbells on this exercise. Again, I have a tendency to use a spotter on this movement for a maximum of 8 to 10 repetitions.

From here, I'll go on to what I call a shaping exercise, which could be anything from pec-deck flyes to cable crossovers to weighted dips. For dips, I'll work up to three 35-pound dumbbells hanging between my legs for 10 to 12 repetitions.

Dips are not always a finisher for me—I'll sometimes start off my chest routine with them. Again, there's no particular order. The next time my chest workout rolls around, my shaping exercise might well be cable crossovers or pec-deck flyes—one or the other, but never both.

Exercise	Warm-Ups	Sets	Reps	Weight
My Mass-Building Pec Routine				
Incline Barbell				
Presses	2	3	8–10	315–365 lb.
Flat-Bench Flyes	2	3	8–10	75–80 lb.
Flat-Bench Dumbbell				
Presses	2	3	8–10	130 lb.
Weighted Dips	2	3	10–12	105 lb.

Chest Exercises

Incline Barbell Presses

I prefer to do my incline presses on a 45-degree inclined bench, with a stand to take the weight off my arms when they are in the locked-out position. I make it a point to always watch the bar with my eyes and to end the descent two or three inches away from my chin, as opposed to having the bar touch my chest. I use a shoulder-width grip and keep my pecs tense (but not hard) throughout the movement. I inhale as I lower the bar and exhale as I press it up to arms' length overhead.

Flat-Bench Flyes

The flat-bench fly is an incredible movement for sculpting the entire pec area. The primary function of the pectorals is to draw the upper-arm bones (humerus) toward the midline of the body, and dumbbell flyes fulfill this function perfectly. Lie down on a flat bench and, with a dumbbell in each hand, slowly draw your hands up over your chest, making sure to keep a slight bend in your elbows to relieve some of the tension on your elbow joints. Getting a good stretch at the bottom and a tight contraction at the top, I like to keep a nice, smooth action going. The action should be like hugging a barrel.

Flat-Bench Dumbbell Presses

Grasp two moderately weighted dumbbells and sit at the end of a flat exercise bench. Place your feet solidly on the floor on either side of the bench, and then lie back. Rotate your wrists so your palms are facing your feet, and press the

dumbbells together directly above your chest to arms' length. Lower and repeat.

Keep Motivated!

People often ask me what keeps me motivated year in and year out and, especially, from workout to workout. I like to use a form of visualization to spur me on. I envision how I want to look and then train with that image firmly in focus. After all, if you don't know where you're going, it's a rather difficult job to navigate how to get there.

You can see where you've been, personally speaking, but you have to have some kind of vision—or something that triggers that vision—of what you want to be. Then you have to be able to retain that image so that when you go into the gym and you do go under construction, you'll have the motivation necessary to push past that eighth rep.

When I'm doing exercises or hitting poses, I'm frequently looking in the mirror and seeing myself—but I'm visualizing what I remember from way back when I started. Visualization can work for you too. Visualize and bear down in your training, and you'll actualize that vision!

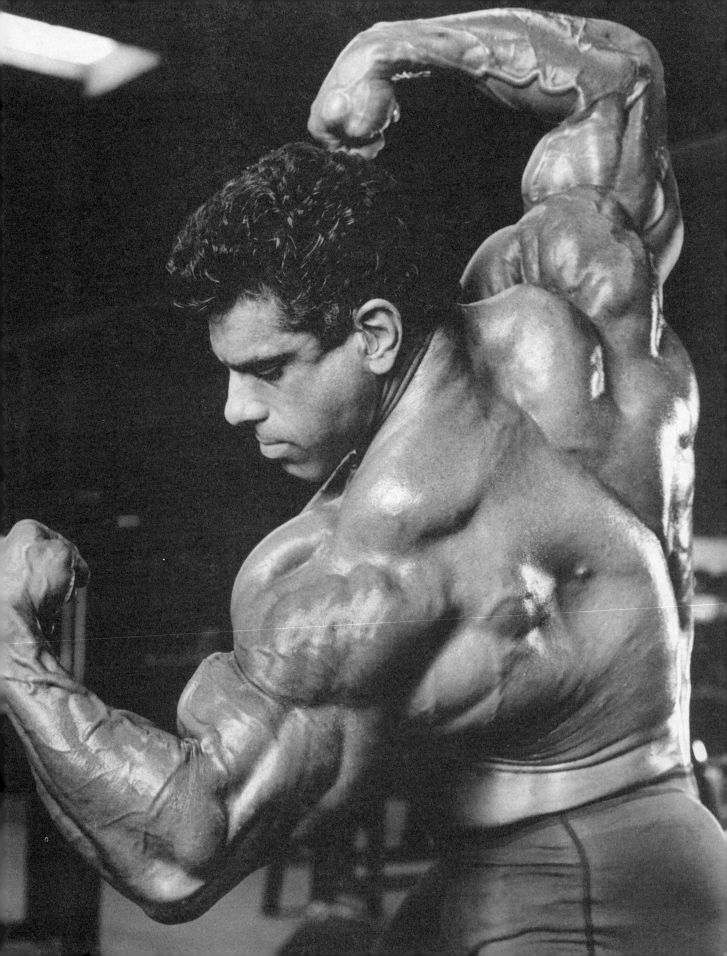

16
Specialization: Back

Complete back development is second only to hip and thigh development as a source of power. Most athletic motions have as their essence the power of the back. In bodybuilding, power is secondary to pure development, but a lot can be learned from power lifters and weight lifters about the basics of athletic power.

I've used the fundamentals of these two sports to enhance my own back training. A key point is that you cannot stop with just a powerful back, which is usually concerned mostly with thickness of the erector spinae muscles. Fully developed latissimus dorsi (or "lats") and all of the small but very important muscles that articulate the shoulder blades add immeasurably to the detail and awe-inspiring sight of a fully developed back.

This chapter covers all aspects of developing a thick, wide, and powerful back. The emphasis is on the basics that have given me the foundation of my development, which I've grouped according to three major components. The correct application of these time-tested ideas will assure you of maximum gains.

I urge you, as in other areas, to make haste slowly with your back program. The penalty for too much enthusiasm and incorrect performance can be months of recuperation from an injury

that should never have happened. The back can be developed to an incredible degree, but it will always be the most injury-prone part of your body.

Always concentrate on keeping your lats contracted as you train them; make sure to pull with the elbows instead of with the biceps. Really focus on pulling with your lats, and view your hands and arms simply as hooks to connect your lats to the resistance.

I should mention at this point that I'm a big believer in using wrist straps on my exercises in order to ensure that the smaller forearm muscles don't become a weak link to the much larger and stronger back muscles during my training.

The exercises in this section are the ones that I have used over the years. My favorites are always in my routines, whereas the secondary movements move about from workout to workout. I will stress again that there are no shortcuts. If you try to move from a novice to an intermediate routine before your body is ready, you will not speed up your progress and may open yourself up to overtraining and injury. Follow the rules and listen to your body, and you will develop the back of your dreams.

Suggested back routines are included at the end of the chapter.

It doesn't really matter whether you start your back training from the lumbar up or from the traps on down; the important thing is that you work up to your top poundage over four or five sets so that you're giving your absolute all to each and every exercise. That way, you'll know that each aspect of your back will be getting all the attention that it deserves—and that the judges have come to expect.

The First Component: Width

Before I launch into my width-training mode, I make sure that I get warmed up properly, which always involves stretching. It would be easy to pull or tear a muscle by just launching into a heavy workout when my muscles are cold. Being a professional, I can't afford to let that happen, so I'll spend a solid 10 minutes stretching and just generally warming up (see "Warm Up Before You Work Out" in Chapter 9).

Wide-Grip Pulldowns

When I say "wide-grip," don't think I'm using some great exaggerated grip. I don't often go

much wider than a shoulder-width grip, as I feel that this position really helps to pull at the lats, which, in effect, are your "width" muscles. I'll get a good stretch and then pull the bar all the way down until it's touching my upper pecs. I'll hold this peak contraction for a two-count and then let the resistance pull my arms back to the starting position. I've always found imagery to be a big help in performing this movement, so I'll envision myself up onstage hitting a rear double-biceps pose—just reaching up, pulling down, and flexing! Don't rock your body back and forth when doing this exercise, however, as you want your lats—not your lower back—to do the work.

Sets: 4–5
Reps: 12–15

One-Arm Dumbbell Rows

Another great width builder is one-arm dumbbell rows. I like to perform this one with one knee on a bench, while supporting my body with the opposite hand. I make a point of gripping the inner portion of the bench for even greater stability, and I always keep the dumbbell angled up toward me in order to get an extra tug on the lats. Then it's simply a matter of going forward, getting a maximum stretch, pulling the weight into the hip, contracting the muscle hard, and putting a bit of hip thrust into the movement to torque it high.

Sets: 4–5
Reps: 12–15

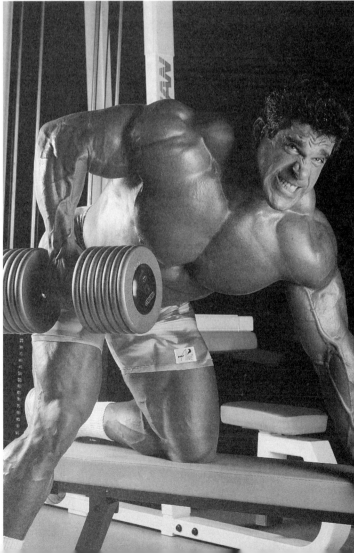

The Second Component: Rhomboids

Seated Rows (Hammer Rows)

The first exercise I'll select for my detail work is seated cable rows on the Hammer Row machine. I'll let the handles take my arms forward, giving my lats a super stretch. I'll get the maximum stretch my scapula will allow before coming back to a 90-degree position and pulling the bar into the lower portion of my pectoralis major muscles.

Sets: 4–5
Reps: 12–15

Seated Cable Rows (Parallel-Grip Handle)

This exercise is not unlike the previous one, only this time I'll use a parallel-grip attachment. The beauty of doing this exercise with the parallel-grip handle is that you can raise or lower the handle's position to achieve the desired result. If you raise your arms, you're hitting your upper back, while if you lower them, you're targeting the central region. I focus on the latter aspect when I perform this exercise, as it gives me that much-desired feature of intricacy that is needed onstage for back shots to be successful. Just like with a straight bar, I'll finish the movement at a 90-degree angle so that I'm not engaging the lower back. Instead, I'm keeping the stress on the middle to upper back region.

Sets: 4–5
Reps: 12–15

The Third Component:
The Erectors

I don't think there's a professional bodybuilder competing today worth his pro card who doesn't include some form of hyperextension or deadlift in his training schedule. I'm certainly a strong advocate of hitting my "lowers"!

I'll use either hypers, regular deadlifts, or bent-knee deadlifts. Not all are done on the same day, mind you; I'll pick maybe two per workout.

Hyperextensions

If I choose hyperextensions, I have two ways to do them: either with a broomstick across the back of my neck or, on heavy days, with a barbell that is preset to weigh 80 pounds. Let me tell you, 12 reps with 80 pounds across your back hurts and is pretty darn shocking to your lumbar area!

Sets: 4
Reps: 12

Bent-Knee Deadlifts

If I'm doing bent-knee deadlifts, I'll make a point of keeping my knees slightly bent and flexed throughout the movement to throw the tension on the lower back region and the erectors. Apart from that, it's the same as standard deadlifting. I don't go as heavy with the bent-knee version as I do with standard deadlifting because the object is to get that hard, contracted flexing of the erector spinae. However, you'll also feel some tension in the glutes and hamstring regions.

Sets: 4

Reps: 10

Back Routines

Novice Routine

(No training experience)

First Month—*Barbell Rows: 1 set of 12 reps, 1 set of 8 reps.*

Second Month—*Barbell Rows: 3 sets of 12/10/8 reps.*

Third Through Fifth Month—*Barbell Rows: 4 sets of 12/10/8/6 reps. Wide-Grip Lat Pulldowns: 3 sets of 12/8/6 reps.*

Sixth Through Twelfth Month—*Barbell Rows: 3 sets of 12/8/6 reps. Wide-Grip Lat Pulldowns: 3 sets of 12/8/6 reps. Hyperextensions: 3 sets of 15/12/8 reps.*

Intermediate Routine

(After at least one year of steady training)

Deadlifts: 4 sets of 12/8/6/6 reps.

Any vertical Wide-Grip Pulldowns: 4 sets of 12/10/8/6 reps.

Any rowing motion (barbell, dumbbell, floor pulley, etc.): 4 sets of 12/10/8/6 reps.

I usually do the intermediate routine most of the year, and it has been very effective for me. If I wanted to get into contest shape or perhaps specialize on my back for 60 days, I would do my advanced routine, which would include the addition of either another lower-back movement or possibly another vertical pulling movement if I wanted to concentrate on more width. At this stage of the game, my routine is very much individualized and instinctive. I vary the routine from workout to workout depending on how I feel.

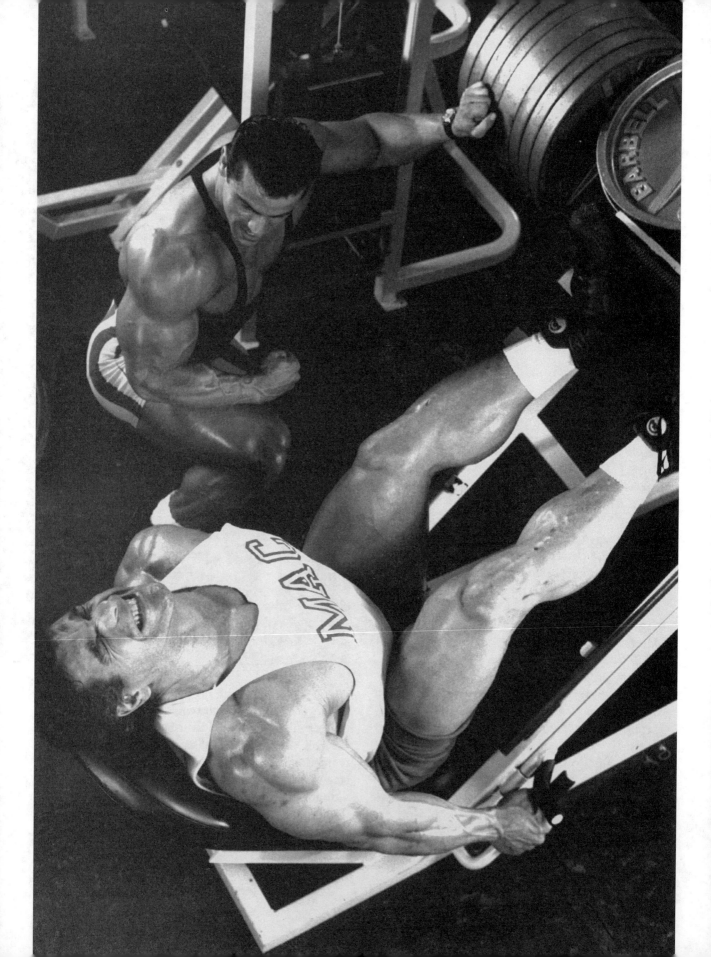

17
Specialization: Legs

By the age of 19, I had been bodybuilding for five years or so, and my upper body had become quite large. But my leg development, particularly my thighs, had not kept pace. I had made the classic beginner's mistake of training to build a showy upper body while neglecting my leg development.

I realized that if I was to succeed as a bodybuilder, I would need to bring my legs into proportion with my upper body. I also knew it would be tough sledding, because my upper body had exploded in growth. For example, my arms had increased from 17" to 20" in just over a year.

During the summer and fall when I was 20, I embarked on a specialized program of heavy leg training. I worked my calves hard, and I squatted until I was blue in the face. As a result, my legs grew tremendously. Within a year, they were perfectly proportioned to the rest of my body, and both my thighs and calves were ripped to shreds.

Bodybuilding history has shown how effective my thigh-specialization workouts were. Within three years, I had won Teenage Mr. America, Mr. America, Mr. International, and Mr. Universe (twice). Had I not chosen to forgo my competitive bodybuilding career to become television's Incredible Hulk, I'm sure I could have won the Mr. Olympia title while still in my mid-20s.

If your thigh development is lagging a little—or even if it isn't, but you wish to improve size and muscularity—I'm sure that some of my thigh-training secrets will benefit you. Thigh training is extremely hard work, but the rewards make the hard work worthwhile.

Thigh strength is directly related to thigh size. The full squat is the basic thigh exercise in this regard, and the heavier you can squat for five to six reps (or more) per set, the greater will be your thigh development.

At the beginning and intermediate levels of training, the only exercise you will need to do for your thighs is the squat. Typically, a beginner can do three or four sets of 8–10 reps in the squat. You will see results even if you use a constant weight for every set, but it is advisable to warm up by using a moderate weight for your first set, then add 10–15 pounds to the bar for each successive set.

Intermediate bodybuilders should pyramid their reps and weights when squatting. Pyramiding, as explained in Chapter 10, means you decrease the reps and increase the training poundage with each successive set of an exercise. This is an excellent way to build both power and mass when doing a basic exercise for any body part. Pyramiding allows you to warm up thoroughly, do some mid-range reps for shape and muscle quality, and finally get in some low-rep sets for mass and power.

Here's a typical pyramiding routine that an intermediate bodybuilder can use. The weights have been chosen arbitrarily and are intended only to show how poundages increase during a pyramid workout.

Pyramiding Squat Routine

Set	Reps	Weight
1	12	135 lb.
2	10	185 lb.
3	8	225 lb.
4	6	255 lb.
5	4	280 lb.
6	2–3	300 lb.

On this pyramiding program, you'll find that your strength and size will increase very quickly. In fact, you should be able to add 10 pounds to your squat each week for a year.

At the intermediate level of bodybuilding, you can begin doing leg curls to fill out your hamstrings. You can also do a few sets of leg extensions to shape and define your thighs. Eventually, you should do the leg extensions at the beginning of your workout to thoroughly warm up your knees and thighs prior to doing heavy squats.

Considering all of these suggestions for intermediate-level training, here is a good all-around thigh workout.

Thigh Routine

Exercise	Sets	Reps
Squats	6	12–2
Leg Extensions	3–4	8–10
Leg Curls	4–5	8–10

This routine can be used steadily for one year. Since my thighs were lagging so badly in my late teens, I had to embark on a superconcentrated specialized thigh routine. I decided to train only my thighs in two of my workouts each week and to work the rest of my body in my four other weekly training sessions. I resolved to concentrate on my squats, persistently increasing my squat weights by 10–20 pounds each week.

Here is the thigh workout I used so successfully when I was 21.

Specialized Thigh Routine

Exercise	Sets	Reps
Squats	6–8	15–2
Leg Presses	4–5	12–4
Leg Extensions	4–5	10–12
Leg Curls	6–8	10–12

This workout was effective for building up my thighs. I still do a workout similar to this, although now I do fewer total sets, because my thighs are up to par with the rest of my body.

A bodybuilder preparing for a competition should do fewer squats and more isolation movements to bring out maximum thigh cuts. Peak-contraction exercises become particularly important during contest preparation. And while I personally don't like the technique, many bodybuilders will superset (or even triset) their thigh exercises. Finally, most bodybuilders do many more sets prior to a contest than in the off-season.

Here's how I typically trained my thighs prior to a competition.

Pre-Contest Thigh Routine		
Exercise	**Sets**	**Reps**
Front Squats	5–6	10–15
Hack Squats	4–5	10–15
Leg Extensions	4–5	10–15
Leg Curls	5–6	10–15
Lunges	3–4	10–15

This type of routine maintained my thigh mass while dramatically increasing my leg shape and definition.

Undeniably, developing a good pair of legs takes discipline and determination. You'll leave plenty of sweat at the squat rack in the process. But with consistent hard work, any bodybuilder will be able to achieve excellent thigh development.

What follows is the "how to" in order to get the most out of the exercises I've just touched upon.

Exercise Descriptions

Squats

The squat is the basic thigh movement. It boosts the body's metabolism and helps you gain lean muscle mass. Many bodybuilders call the squat the "king of bodybuilding exercises" (see p. 61).

Start with your feet set at about shoulder width, with your toes angled outward at about 45 degrees on each side. Rest a heavy barbell behind your neck across your trapezius muscles, and balance it in place with your hands. Stand erect, and focus your gaze at shoulder level throughout the movement. This will keep your head up as you squat and prevent your back from rounding during the movement. Tense your back muscles, and keep them tight for the whole set.

From this basic starting position, squat down until your thighs are below an imaginary line drawn parallel to the floor. As you squat down, your torso should be held as erect as possible and your thighs should travel outward at a 45-degree angle directly over the line of your feet. Do not bounce at the bottom of the movement; simply stop the movement once your thighs are past a position parallel to the floor, and then return to the starting point by straightening your thighs. Repeat the movement for the required number of repetitions.

You should also be sure to wear a weightlifting belt when doing your squats. If you expe-rience difficulty doing your squats flat-footed (a sign of ankle inflexibility), you can rest your heels on a 2" × 4" board while squatting.

Front Squats (Variation)

This movement is very similar to standard squats, except that the bar is held across the upper chest and shoulders during the movement, rather than across the upper back and shoulders. Front squats place more stress on the muscles just above the knees than do regular squats.

Leg Presses

Many bodybuilders use leg presses in place of squats, because leg presses place less strain on the lower back. Start by lying with your head at the lower end of an angled board and your hips directly under the movable platform. Place your feet on the board at shoulder width, and straighten your legs. Release the safety stops on the machine. Bend your legs as fully as possible, then straighten them. Repeat for the required number of repetitions.

Hack Squats

I've found this to be an excellent movement for enhancing thigh cuts and shape. Place your feet on the angled platform with your heels about 12 inches apart and your toes pointed outward at 45-degree angles on each side. Bend your legs fully, and rest your back against the sliding platform. Grasp the handles beside your hips to steady your back against the sliding platform. From this position, straighten and bend your legs for the required number of repetitions.

Lunges

The lunge is a basic movement for shaping the thighs and enhancing definition, and it should be used prior to a competition. It's particularly good for improving upper-thigh muscularity.

Start in the same position as you would for a regular squat, but use a much lighter barbell. Step forward two-and-a-half to three feet with your left foot (your toes should be pointed directly forward). Keeping your right leg straight, fully bend your left knee. At the bottom position of the movement, your left knee should be four to six inches ahead of your left ankle, and your right knee should be two to three inches above the floor. Push hard with your left thigh muscles to return to the starting point. Do your next repetition with your right leg forward, and alternate legs for the full number of repetitions.

Leg Extensions

Sit at the end of a leg-extension unit so the backs of your knees are right against the edge of the pad. Hook the insteps of your feet under the lower set of roller pads. To keep your body in position during the movement, grasp the handles provided next to your hips or the sides of the bench. From this basic starting point, simply extend your legs slowly until they are completely straight. Hold this position for a count of two or three to assure that you have a peak contraction. Slowly lower the roller pad back to the starting point, and repeat the movement for the required number of repetitions.

Leg Curls

Leg curls are the best exercise for developing the hamstring muscles at the backs of your thighs. Lie face down on the leg-curl machine so your knees are against the padded surface at the edge of the bench. Hook your heels under the upper set of roller pads, and fully straighten your legs. To steady your body in this position, grasp the handles beside and below your shoulders or the edges of the bench. Then slowly bend your legs as fully as possible. Hold this position two or three seconds for a peak-contraction effect, then

lower the roller pad back to the starting point. Repeat for the desired number of repetitions. There is also an equipment variation in which leg curls can be performed from a standing position, using one leg at a time.

If you perform these exercises exactly as they are prescribed in this chapter, you'll be more than pleased with the way your thighs will respond.

18
Specialization: Arms

As you plan your workouts, always keep in mind that what I'm presenting to you in the specialization series in this book are sample routines. They are not the *only* routines you should ever try, but rather guidelines to direct your training efforts.

It's important to keep changing your routines around from time to time, as this keeps your body in a state of confusion and doesn't allow it to become complacent with movements that are repeated day in and day out. Mix things up a bit, and not only your body but also your mind will thank you for it.

Now, let's get on to the business of arm training.

The visual impact of the arms is a product of the balance of the individual parts. I always strive to keep a balance among biceps, triceps, and both parts of the forearms. While the whole arm is worked to a certain degree with torso work, it does take extra concentrated effort to ensure proper arm proportion and size.

This chapter covers my favorite arm exercises and their performance and describes ways to integrate my ideas into a personal plan to make the most of the arm shape you possess.

Everyone has a challenge to create the best possible arms for his or her structure. Not everyone can have 23" arms like mine, but then again, you're probably not 6'5" and 300 pounds! Your individual potential will determine the correct path to your best development. The arm routines outlined cover different stages of experience. If you're a beginner with less than six months of regular training, don't try to follow my intermediate or advanced programs. If you try to move too quickly to the advanced level, you'll only hinder your progress. You can't build a strong, enduring structure on an incomplete foundation. Many times, I see positive enthusiasm for training turn into overtraining, injuries, and, ultimately, lost interest in training because of this lack of patience. There are no shortcuts. The intelligent application of proven ideas is the only way.

Progress is the result of doing your best in each workout. If you don't put forth your maximum effort each time, there's no way to catch up, and you will be that much further from attaining your goals. I fight the "I'll do better on the next set" gremlin just as you do. I beat back that little fella, and so should you.

Biceps

Barbell Curls

I always work the basic or muscle-belly exercise first in my biceps routine because it is the largest part and therefore should have the fullest access to my energy for maximum growth. The barbell curl should be part of every routine, as it is the key to attaining maximum biceps size. I use either a straight bar or an EZ-curl bar, depending on how I feel that particular training session. Either way, the belly of the biceps gets the same work.

At the start of the movement, your forearms should be fully extended and the biceps should be stretched. It's important to start from this position so that you get full development from the movement. I often see people swing the weight from this starting position and thereby cut off all the work for the lower belly of the biceps. Complete movements build complete development.

As the bar begins to move, I'll concentrate on keeping my torso erect and my elbows at my sides. The movement of the curl must be very smooth so that the biceps get the full benefit of the movement and also to guard against injury. As you reach the top or fully contracted position, guard against the urge to lean back. The correct thing to do is stay erect throughout the whole movement. This is not a back movement; the work should be done as completely as possible by your biceps. The top position should be intensified by contracting the biceps for a second until they almost cramp. Always lower the bar slowly and under complete control to the starting position. I sometimes use a slight cheat on the last two reps in an attempt to force added growth. However, I always lower the bar slowly, even on these cheat reps.

Preacher Curls

I begin this exercise with the barbell at my neck and my biceps contracted to the point of almost cramping. My chest is tight against the bench,

and my feet are firmly braced. I'll keep my torso and legs in this position throughout the entire movement to ensure a solid base and total isolation of my biceps.

At the midpoint of the movement, the stress level begins to become heavy. Always keep the bar under control. If you can't, the weight is too heavy. As you approach the fully extended position, the biceps should never be allowed to relax, and tension should be kept on them all the time. Never bounce out of the extended position, as that is an invitation to disaster. That bounce could put an early end to your bodybuilding career by tearing a muscle.

The preacher curl works the whole biceps, with particular emphasis on the lower biceps and brachialis. If you have short, high biceps, put special importance on this movement so that you can create a fuller look to your arms, especially in the hanging position. I usually use the EZ-curl bar on this movement, but I sometimes use the straight bar for variety. My hand spacing is about shoulder width, with my elbows in line with my hands. Do not let your elbows slide outward during the movement, especially during the bottom or extreme-stretch part.

Occasionally, I'll substitute dumbbell preacher curls, which I find to be a very effective upper-arm developer as well. You will find that you cannot use as much weight with dumbbells as you can with the barbell version, since you have another problem to contend with—balance. I use basically the same style as for the barbell version, but I'll start at the bottom with my hands turned out and continue with them in that position. This works the long head of the biceps more than the barbell version.

Incline Dumbbell Curls

I prefer a 45-degree incline bench for this movement, as it allows me to isolate the biceps and still be relatively comfortable. I keep my head against the bench and incline with my torso as I perform the movement. It's important that you hold this position throughout the duration of the set. It not only aids in the isolation of the biceps and therefore their development but will also guard against any tendency of a trapezius pull, which can happen if you turn your head to either side

while under extreme stress. Even when you're fighting for that last rep or two, always stay under control and in position. Staying in position and under control is an act of deep focus. If you find yourself straying into a sloppy, dangerous style, you'll know that you are not getting everything possible out of the movement and are diverting energy into nonessential contortions.

You should feel a definite stretch in the biceps at the start of the movement. Smoothly begin the rep by rotating your hands outward until the palms are facing out and your elbows are pinned tightly to your sides. This is the point of maximum stress, and you must be thinking deeply into your biceps to finish the rep and pass through this "sticking point." Continue to rotate the hands until you're in the fully contracted position. If this movement is done correctly,

you'll feel it in every inch of your biceps, with special emphasis on the belly of the muscle and also at the peak.

Pulley Cable Curls

Pulley cable curls involve more of a continuous-tension movement but with a lot of the same characteristics as the dumbbell curl. Because I like working one arm at a time for deeper concentration, I sometimes use this exercise as an alternative to dumbbell concentration curls.

I'll stand next to the pulley machine so that the force is as vertical as possible. Because this movement provides continuous tension, you can really feel the deep muscle burn that tells you something good is happening! This burn is due to an accumulation of lactic acid in the muscle as it's being worked. Because of the continuous ten-

sion, the muscle doesn't have a chance to clear out these natural products of muscular work. It will probably be necessary to shake the muscle in between sets to hasten the recovery process and to stop the tendency to cramp that an accumulation of lactic acid can cause. The movement is smoothly performed with a rotation of the hand until the correct position is reached.

Always lower the weight under complete control and no faster than you raised it. If you hurry the movement, you'll lose some of the benefit. Every rep of every movement is important, so don't shortchange yourself with poor style. Every movement is an investment in your new physique.

Concentration Curls

The concentration curl allows for total isolation of the biceps, which is necessary if you are to get all of the peak that is possible out of your particular biceps structure. You cannot make a totally flat biceps as peaked as Arnold Schwarzenegger's, but you can enhance the look of the peak if you carefully follow my description of this exercise. Remember that one of the great things about bodybuilding is you are in control of the growth of your development, even though the maximum potential is genetically predetermined. Everyone can improve the development of his or her biceps with the correct program.

My technique in this movement is to keep my arm free of my knee and to perform the curl in a

totally unsupported style. I feel that by using the biceps in this manner, I'm forcing all the small stabilizing muscles to work hard also and therefore give me better overall development. The starting position is quite stable, and I will not vary this body position throughout the movement. The only thing that moves is the forearm and the dumbbell. No swing, no cheat, just total concentration and pure movement.

As I begin the movement, I again begin the all-important rotation of the hand. As I get into the contracted position, my hand is completely twisted, my little finger is almost touching my deltoid, and my biceps are screaming in anguish. This twist and contraction are essential to the success of the movement. Slowly lower the

dumbbell and reverse the sequence of the hand rotation until you are again in the starting position. That's one rep and the beginning of a better-shaped biceps.

The concentration curl is a great movement, but only if you need it. If you already have (genetically) short, high-peaked biceps, don't spend your time on this one. Invest it in the preacher curl. As I will show you in the section on specific routines, the best routine for you is the one that gives you the best development. I am different from you, and I can only lay out the ground rules which you must then personalize. In the final analysis, each of us is our own coach. Instinctive training becomes effective only when we understand the basics and who we are physically.

Triceps

The triceps muscle makes up more than two-thirds of the bulk of the upper arm, so knowing the best exercises and how they are performed is essential to attaining complete development in your upper arms. Don't confuse biceps work with total arm work—it's only part of the story, and the smaller part at that.

Lying Triceps Extensions

This is the most effective triceps movement I've ever performed. I lie down on an exercise bench with my feet at one end and my head just off the other side. I use a shoulder-width grip on an EZ-curl bar, both because it affords the correct hand spacing for me, and the slightly angled grip seems to get the triceps better with less strain on the elbows than with a normal straight bar. I'll lower the bar slowly with no swing and with my back flat on the bench. As I get to the bottom position, I'll use a slight pullover-type movement. The pullover is actually a smooth movement of the elbows in a short arc. It isn't a cheating move; on the contrary, it adds to the effectiveness of the exercise. By keeping the elbows slightly back, rather than straight up as is usually done, I find that I get a better feeling from the movement. The continuous tension adds a new dimension to the exercise.

Triceps Pushdowns

I use an overhead pulley for this movement, which provides continuous tension on the whole triceps. I sometimes choose a bar that is slightly angled for a change of pace, but I typically use a straight bar. I prefer a narrow hand-spacing so that my elbows are tightly at my sides. Your elbows should not move from this position throughout the entire movement. By keeping the elbows under control, you centralize the force and mental energy into the triceps. I'll slowly press the bar down until my elbows are fully extended. By forcefully contracting the triceps at the completion of the movement, I almost get a muscle cramp because of my intense concentration.

Ideally, this movement is one continuous motion with a pause at the finished position as your mind extracts the last bit of benefit from the exercise. To really feel this ultimate contraction at the finish of the movement, focus on your hands. I have found that while you cannot actually rotate your hands on the bar, the act of thinking about it intensifies the quality of the contraction.

Close-Grip Bench Presses

I consider this movement an advanced exercise to be attempted only by experienced body-builders. The reason is that it places a tremendous strain on the wrists. I always use the EZ-curl bar for this one, as the hand position seems to alleviate some of that stress. I use a narrow grip, and the bar is held directly over my chest. As I lower the bar, my elbows go directly to the sides and my hands end up across my mid-pecs. I'll press the bar slowly, and mentally contract the triceps at the top of the movement. It is important that you do the movement very smoothly so that you get the most for your triceps with the least harm to your wrists. I really like this movement for adding size around the lower portions of the triceps.

One-Arm Pulley Triceps Extensions

This exercise allows you to engage in deep concentration, and because of the freedom of hand movement, you can get a very complete contraction. I'll hold the handle in a palms-up grip and slowly extend my forearm, rotating my hand so that I'm pressing down to get the final peak contraction. Then I'll slowly return to the starting position.

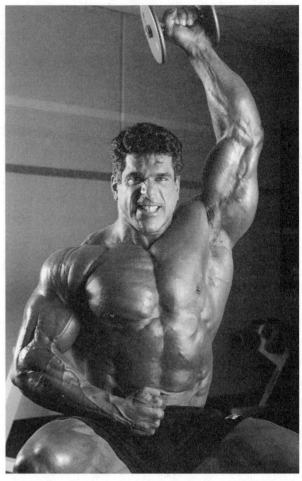

One-Arm Dumbbell Extensions

The dumbbell is an excellent tool for building big triceps. While seated, hold the dumbbell behind your head and slowly extend the forearm until it is completely locked out. This movement works all three heads of the triceps very intensely. It is important to really force the contraction at the finished position. Don't just bounce out of the contracted position—feel the triceps almost cramp on every repetition.

Reverse Curls

The upper or top portion of the forearms is most easily developed with the reverse curl. My grip is narrow, and my elbows are held tight to my sides. A common error is to let the elbows rise with the movement and thereby change it into a cleaning movement. Keep the elbows in, and isolate the tops of the forearms. Of course, you are working some of the biceps and the brachialis as well, but by keeping the grip narrow and concentrating on the movement, you will get the most out of it.

One-Arm Triceps Kickbacks with Dumbbell
I typically use this movement only as a pre-contest "finishing" exercise. I'll bend over so that my upper body is parallel to the floor. I then extend my arm behind me in a steady, controlled manner until the contraction is complete. This movement is very strict. Its purpose is to totally delineate the triceps and hopefully add those very important cross-striations to all three heads of the triceps. While diet is the most important component of attaining ultimate muscularity and detail, I find that when I add in a very specialized isolation movement such as this one, I get the best results.

Forearms

Many arms are not as impressive as they should be because of a lack of proportionate forearm development. While the forearms can be more stubborn than the biceps or triceps, they will improve if you persistently use the correct approach.

Designing an Arm Routine

I prefer to work the biceps and forearms on one day and the triceps by themselves on another day. The so-called push-pull workout makes a lot of sense to me, and it is a format that I usually use. As I said earlier, I try different routines from time to time as my development and emotions dictate. This instinctive training style can be acquired only by first trying the proven methods and then "listening" carefully to the way your body reacts to the different exercises and exercise combinations. I continually learn from workouts. Analyze your arm development to see what is needed.

Three-Step Novice Routine
Mondays and Thursdays

If you are a beginner, you should work your biceps and forearms with your thighs and back on Mondays and Thursdays. Two workouts per week give the greatest possible growth. More often than not, the move from two to three workouts per week stops progress and produces overtraining. I very rarely use a weekly three-workout-per-body-part schedule for anything but the most serious competition preparation, and then only for a short period of time.

- During the *first month*, you'll do two sets of barbell curls, 8–10 reps. Your first set should be a warm-up with about 70 percent of your best weight for 10 reps. The second set should be performed with a weight that is heavy enough that only 8 reps can be performed. If you can get 10 reps in good style, increase the weight by five pounds. You'll then do two sets of palms-up wrist curls, 12–15 reps. Use one as the warm-up set as above, and go all out on the second one.
- The *second and third months*, increase the sets to three, adding another set between your warm-up set and your go-for-broke set.
- *Months four through six* should see you expanding the biceps/forearm program to five sets of each of the two movements.

Again, the progressive weight system should be fully utilized.

Tuesdays and Fridays

The triceps are worked on Tuesdays and Fridays with calves, delts, abs, and chest. Always work the arms (biceps, triceps, and forearms) at the end of the regular workout routines. If you attempt to work the arms first, you will discover that you can't work the torso with much efficiency because of the resulting fatigue.

- The *first month* I would do two sets of lying triceps presses. The first set would function as a warm-up, and I would perform 12 to 15 reps. The second set would be a little heavier, with about 8 to 10 reps being the maximum. If you can get 10 reps in good style on the second set, then add two 1.25-pound plates for the next workout.
- The *second and third months* will see you go to three sets of the lying triceps movement. You should use a weight that is light enough for you to get 12 to 15 reps on the first set. Add a little weight for the second set of 10 to 12 reps, and then add again for the final set of 8 to 10 reps.
- During *months four through six*, you will expand the number of sets to five. Use the weight-addition method as before. You should be reaching your maximum weight on your fifth set. Do not let the reps fall below six. If you cannot get six good reps on any set, lower the weight.

In review, the workouts would look like the following.

Mondays and Thursdays
First Month
Barbell Curls: 2 sets of 8–10 reps.
Palms-Up Wrist Curls: 2 sets of 8–10 reps.
Second and Third Month
Barbell Curls: 3 sets of 8–10 reps.
Palms-Up Wrist Curls: 3 sets of 10–15 reps.

Fourth Through Sixth Month
Barbell Curls: 5 sets of 8–10 reps.
Palms-Up Wrist Curls: 5 sets of 8–15 reps.

Tuesdays and Fridays
First Month
Lying Triceps Presses: 2 sets of 8–15 reps.
Second and Third Month
Lying Triceps Presses: 3 sets of 8–15 reps.
Fourth Through Sixth Month
Lying Triceps Presses: 5 sets of 8–15 reps.

Intermediate Routine

After you have worked through my novice sequence, you should be ready for a step up to an intermediate routine, which I divide into two stages.

Stage one is the addition of another exercise to each of the three basic movements that are used in the novice routine. We hold onto the basic movements because they are the foundation of all arm work. For this stage we add preacher curls to your biceps day and also palms-down wrist curls to the forearm work. You will do four sets of each of the movements. Your triceps day will be expanded by the addition of triceps pressdowns. This stage one routine will be continued for six months.

Stage two of the intermediate cycle is the addition of another movement to each of the three subsections that make up the arm. For the biceps, I would add the incline-bench dumbbell curl for four sets of 8–10 reps. For the triceps, add the seated or standing French press for four sets of 8–10 reps. The forearms will need the reverse curl for four sets of 8–12 reps.

The two stages of the intermediate routine would look like the following.

Mondays and Thursdays
Stage One—Six Months
Barbell Curls: 4 sets of 8–10 reps.
Preacher Curls: 4 sets of 8–10 reps.
Palms-Up Wrist Curls: 4 sets of 8–15 reps.
Palms-Down Wrist Curls: 4 sets of 8–15 reps.

Stage Two—Six Months
Barbell Curls: 4 sets of 8–10 reps.
Preacher Curls: 4 sets of 8–10 reps.
Incline-Bench Dumbbell Curls: 4 sets of 8–10 reps.
Reverse Curls: 4 sets of 8–12 reps.
Palms-Down Wrist Curls: 4 sets of 8–12 reps.
Palms-Up Wrist Curls: 4 sets of 8–12 reps.

Tuesdays and Fridays
Stage One—Six Months
Lying Triceps Presses: 4 sets of 8–10 reps.
Triceps Pressdowns: 4 sets of 8–10 reps.

Stage Two—Six Months
Lying Triceps Presses: 4 sets of 8–10 reps.
Triceps Pressdowns: 4 sets of 8–10 reps.
Standing French Presses with Barbell: 4 sets of 8–10 reps.

Advanced Stage

The advanced stage is really a stage of specialization. I've described more movements in this chapter than are included in the preceding routines because it was my intention to list all the arm movements that I've ever used. You should be developing your own personal exercise philosophy by now and should use this instinct to tailor my ideas to your own program.

The advanced stage is also one of analysis. Look critically at your arms. Look at the three major areas within the structure and at the overall symmetry of the arms in relation to the rest of the body. If the arms are getting too big for the deltoids—a common flaw, by the way—cut back on the amount of arm work you are performing. If your arms are lagging behind the rest of your body, don't increase the arm work; instead, cut down on the other work so that you can give your arms a chance to grow. The stagnation of arm growth is usually due to overwork on the total routine.

You can achieve only one goal at a time, and you can specialize on only one body part at a time. Focus your energy, and you'll achieve the arms of your dreams.

19
Specialization: Abdominals

The abdominals, in conjunction with the serratus, intercostals, and obliques, comprise the focus of the physique from the front. When viewing a physique contest, the eye is immediately drawn to the center of the body, so the complete development of this area is the key to great first impressions on the posing stage. Without full development and muscular definition in this area, a physique has a great deal missing, and even the uninitiated in the sport will recognize this fact. Never neglect abdominal development!

Because the general thickness of the muscles in this area is so shallow, you must be relatively lean to show them. You may have them, but if they're covered with even one-quarter inch of fat, they'll disappear. This is in contrast to, say, the biceps, which will retain its visible shape to a much higher degree even if you are a little fat.

The point is that having abdominal/serratus/intercostal development is one thing and being able to see it is another. Diet is the most important factor in being able to "see" your abs. The exercises that I describe in this chapter are the keys to development, but diet is the key to definition.

You will not be able to keep rock-hard, visibly etched abdominals at all times because as you gain overall body size and weight, you put on a little fat. Continue to work the muscles while on a gaining program, and when you decide to get really cut up, the muscles will be there. Don't misunderstand me: don't get fat in the abdominal region, but rather a little smooth, which is acceptable during the gaining stages. If your abs disappear, get on a fat-loss diet until they are fully visible. Never go on to a gaining cycle unless your abs are clearly etched. If you do, you'll succeed only in getting fatter, and you'll have a difficult and long road back to a lean look.

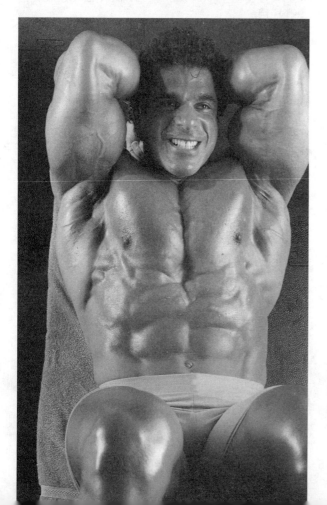

Ab Exercises

Crunches

My favorite upper-abdominal exercise is the crunch. This movement isolates the upper section of the abs like no other. To perform this movement, I'll lie on my back on either a bench or the floor and elevate my feet on something (usually a bench if I'm on the floor). Keeping my back flat, I really don't pull up with my legs at all during the movement. Instead, I'll stabilize my hips so that more concentration can be directed onto the abs. I slowly curl my trunk upward until my shoulder blades just leave the ground. This is the point of maximum muscular contraction, and the upper two segments of the abs will feel as if they'll pop through your skin! I try to hold the contracted position for at least a count of two and very slowly return to the starting position.

The entire movement should be very smooth with no jerkiness whatsoever. On each rep, I just barely touch my back to the floor or bench. I keep constant tension on the area and always attempt to raise myself higher on each rep. This contraction must be just that—no cheating. To better isolate my mind on the abs and to get an even deeper feel from the movement, I will place one or both of my hands on the area and feel the contraction. Deep concentration will measurably heighten the degree of contraction that is possible.

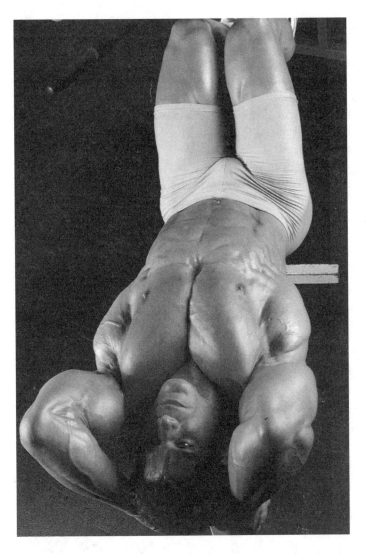

Knee-Ups

Knee-ups, an excellent all-around abdominal exercise, serve two functions, working both the top half of the abs (the sit-up portion) and the lower half (the leg-raise portion). I typically perform the movement without weight, but if you need extra thickness in your abs, you can balance a barbell plate across the insteps of your feet. I keep my whole body under tension and at a 45-degree angle to the ground. Concentration and balance are essential to correct execution. My hands lightly grip the bench, just to aid my balance. Eventually you will be able to do the movement without holding on at all. When you can consistently do your reps without holding

on, you'll notice that this balancing act enhances the development of the exercise. The key is to move not only your legs but also your torso in a "scissoring" type of motion. My torso meets my upper thighs, and I crunch down hard on the upper abs and return to the starting position. This motion will probably be very jerky and unsure in the beginning, but stick with it; eventually it will be smooth and fluid, and you will be able to get the most out of it.

Leg Raises

I prefer to do leg raises while supported upon parallel bars that have special pads specifically for this purpose. Some pads are spaced wider apart than others; if the equipment you use has a wide base on which to rest your elbows, you'll be able to draw your legs up higher, which makes for a fuller contraction. This is primarily a lower-ab exercise, but one that also works the whole area, including the obliques. I try to touch my thighs to my chest on each rep.

A variation on this is that I will twist my hips first to the right and then to the left to better affect the obliques. I will do equal reps for each side and then as many straight-on reps as possible. I usually do 15/15/10 repetitions. There are two other variations that I sometimes use: the leg raise from the parallel-bar dip position and the hanging leg raise from a chin-up bar. The actual execution of the movements is the same, but they all have different feels and therefore different stress points and developments. The hanging version, which is my favorite, gets the intercostal and serratus muscles much better than the other two because the whole torso is forced to stabilize itself throughout the exercise, so all of the small muscles of the torso are worked to the maximum.

Leg Raises on a Flat Bench

This is another excellent movement for the lower abs. I usually go to just parallel to the floor and no lower. If you go farther down than parallel, you run the risk of lower back injury. It also helps to put your hands under your butt for stability. Both of these elements of style help to relieve the back of undue stress. I prefer to look at my abs during this movement, as this enhances my concentration and also contracts the upper part of the abs and adds to the effectiveness of the exercise. If you need more thickness in the lower abs, you can add weight via a small barbell plate attached to your feet by a strap, or attach an ankle pulley. Don't neglect the lower abs when designing a routine.

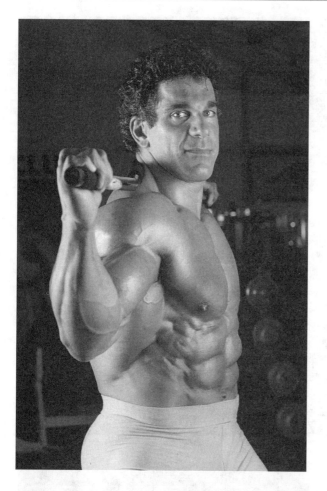

Seated Twists

The seated twist is an excellent oblique-shaping movement. This exercise will give the whole abdominal region a good workout if you do all the variations. I never use anything heavier than an empty exercise bar or a broom handle. I don't like weight in this movement for two reasons: I am not trying to make my waist or obliques larger, and I want to avoid the danger to the spine of twisting with weight. I never twist very far, as an excessive twist is an invitation to a spinal injury.

I perform each rep without much momentum. I try to keep the whole abdominal region flexed mentally on every twist. If you are mentally flexed, you will not be able to do the irrational swinging that passes for so much of the performance of this movement that I see in the gym. If you mindlessly swing to and fro, don't expect the results that are possible with this exercise. I usually incorporate the 45-degree bent-forward variation of this movement each time I do it. The same philosophy goes for this as well: do not swing or deliberately try to touch the left knee with the right elbow, and alternate with the right knee.

Abdominal Routine

The advanced ab routine is one of specialization and contest preparation. I usually add twists to the intermediate routine and cut the rest periods down between sets as much as possible.

Exercise	Sets	Reps
First Month		
Crunches	1	15
Second Month		
Crunches	2	15
Third Month		
Crunches	3	15
Novice		
(Less than six months' training experience)		
Hanging Leg Raises	2	15
Crunches	2	15
Intermediate		
(More than one year of steady training)		
Leg Raises	3	15
Upper-Abdominal Exercise	3	15
Intercostal Pulley Crunches	3	15

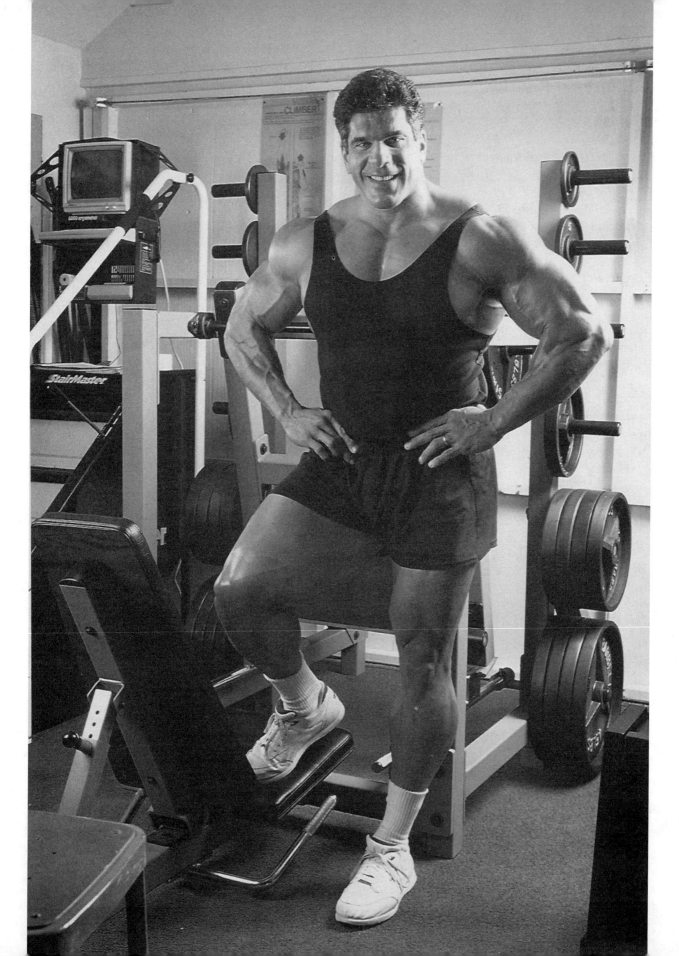

20
The Home Gym

From the outset, the reason anyone should want to have a home gym is that you really want to improve your existing physical condition. You have to *want* to go in there and do some serious—often hard—training. You can't go in with the attitude, "Oh, I have a home gym now, so I'll have some friends over and put on a show." I've got a couple of friends who live in mansions and "think" they have a home gym. They've devoted a room in their house to it, all right, but it's all chrome dumbbells and large multistation exercise units. The rooms look pretty and fancy—but I'm afraid to actually break into a sweat in these places in case I smudge the chrome!

To have a real home gym, you have to ask yourself, "What do I really need?" and "How do I really want to train?" The advantage to having a home facility, depending on your personal situation, is that it provides solutions to typical "go to the gym" problems. You won't always have time to travel to a gym, get changed, wait for people to get off the equipment you hope to use, and then travel back home. If you have a family, it can be hard to justify such an arduous, time-consuming process.

If you have a gym in your own home or garage, however, you can slip in, work out, and shower up before anyone notices you're gone—

any time you want. A home gym is open 24 hours, and you never have to wait in line to use the equipment. Plus, if there is an emergency at home, you're right there to look after things. These days, I think a home gym is the most practical, efficient, and productive answer to getting in shape, building muscle, and not disrupting your life.

In your own gym, you can do circuit training without interruption, select your own music, motivate yourself, and put up your own posters and pictures to inspire you. Also, if you happen to live in the Midwest or another area where winter weather conditions can impede travel, if you were training in a commerical gym, you'd have to forgo your health and fitness pursuits until the weather cleared up. But when you have a gym in your garage or a designated room in your house you simply go out and hit the iron! You can't beat a home gym.

Gains at Home

People who say, "You have to go to a big commercial gym to really make gains" are completely wrong. I believe that you can make any kind of gains you want while training at home.

You just have to stay highly motivated. For me, the fact that I can do whatever I want to do when I enter my home gym is what's important. The whole program is designed by "me" to be used on "my" equipment. I call it my "adult toy room." It's fun, and my workout tools are like toys to me. I'd rather have a home gym and spend my time in the pursuit of improving myself than being in a bar or nightclub drinking or trying to impress people. Home-gym training is a very healthy and productive pursuit.

Ever since I was a kid, I wanted to have "the best" home gym in the world, and all things considered, I've come pretty darn close to achieving it. I have one of the most elaborate home gyms I've ever seen, and I've sunk more than $200,000 into it, but it's my pride and joy. I've been lifting weights for more than 30 years now, and in that time I've learned exactly what you need to put in

your basement, garage, or house for the sake of muscle building. Everything in my gym has been handpicked by me for a specific body part or purpose. Everything is geared toward function; I use it. You won't find any equipment in there gathering dust.

Your Personal "Mecca of Bodybuilding"

While I cite my gym as an example, I realize that it's an extreme one. Not everyone can afford to spend as much money as I've put into my home gym, and not everyone would choose to. It's a personal decision. You have to design and spend according to your own wants and needs. I trained in a home gym in my parents' basement for the bulk of my teenage life, a setup far removed from the kind I own now. Still, I won the Teenage Mr. America training at home in that gym with a lot less equipment than I have now.

Some will say that you should still work out in a professional gym in order to have "professional supervision" during each workout. I'm the last one to knock personal trainers or "trained professionals," but, let's be honest, not everyone wants or can afford one. What then? I never had anyone standing over me and observing my form and improving my technique. I had the same as you do—magazines and books. Now there are even videos to help you learn proper form and exercise execution. You don't need a supervisor, but if you can afford one, by all means sign one up.

The most important thing about a home gym is that it allows you to make a commitment to yourself that you're really going to train. If you're determined to make progress, you will. However, you can't have any distractions. Close the door, be alone in that room, and "train." The home gym is just that—a "home gym." Leave it at that. Don't put flowers in it; don't put up pretty paintings.

Create a gym atmosphere; hang pictures of physique champions to inspire you, but give it that "gym" feel. It's a place of work and dedication, not a social club. The worst course is to put a home gym in half of a garage and leave the other half full of tools and storage materials. Don't mix things up. Make your garage your own personal "Mecca of Bodybuilding," and leave the tools in the shed.

By that I'm not suggesting that you *have* to be a competitive bodybuilder and train to enter contests in order to improve your body or to have a proper home gym. While you do have to be a bodybuilder, you need to be one only to yourself. Bodybuilding simply means "building your body" and taking care of it. It does not mean that you have to go onstage and compete. Weight lifting means you're just lifting weight. That's why when people ask me, "Are you a weight lifter?" I reply, "No, I'm a body 'builder.'" I don't put 500 pounds over my head for a single rep—that's "weight lifting"—an Olympic sport. Bodybuilding is simply looking after your body and keeping it strong and healthy.

The Tools

One of the best aspects of weight training is that you need very little equipment to get results: just a barbell, a squat stand (or rack), and a flat bench. As I mentioned in Chapter 13, when I filmed the movie *Hercules*, I didn't have the luxury of training in a commercial gym—nor, for that matter, in a fully equipped home gym. What I used to build the physique that some have said was the greatest condition ever achieved on screen is exactly what I've described above: a flat bench, a squat rack, and a 315-pound Olympic barbell set.

How did I train each body part with such a meager complement of equipment? Easy—I improvised! There's so much you can do with a barbell, it's almost a miracle muscle-building tool!

This is why I consider the components mentioned here to be the perfect starter gym for people looking to train at home. As most barbell sets come with exercise instruction sheets these days, it's pretty hard to go wrong on this front. A source I strongly recommend is Advance Free Weight Systems, (800) 872-8811; for more advanced training equipment, call Strive Enterprises at (800) 368-6448.

The cost of the starter setup will vary, of course, depending on the brand name and quality. All told, however, you really don't need to spend more than $1,000 on setting up your own personal home gym.

Here's the breakdown:
Barbell/dumbbell set: $40 to $250
Squat stands: $50 to $750
Flat bench: $120 to $250

Remember, your muscles don't need fancy equipment to grow. If you give them progressively greater loads to lift, they'll get bigger and stronger. Those loads can come from a barbell you buy at Sears, a $25,000 machine at your gym, or, for that matter, a suitcase filled with rocks.

Commercial Gyms: What Emily Post Won't Tell You

If you decide to work out in a commercial gym, you don't want to inadvertently anger the club's clientele by breaking rules of etiquette that were probably never explained to you in the first place. Some of these pointers may seem obvious, but after a lifetime of weight training, I'm still amazed by how many people don't follow them.

- *Don't* get uptight with people who happen to have arrived at a given machine or exercise station before you. Your turn will come. If the line is too long at your station, find another exercise to perform. Try leg presses if the squat rack is taken. Do bench presses with dumbbells if the barbell benches are too crowded. Be flexible; you'll always get a good workout.
- *Don't* pose in front of the mirror after every set. We all like to check out our results, but if you don't want to look ridiculous, do it subtly or, better yet, in the privacy of your own home.
- *Don't* yell and scream during your sets. If you have enough energy to make like Tarzan at the squat rack, you've got enough to do (at least!) two more reps.

- *Don't* drop the weights. Every gym has a rule against this, but every gym has guys who think it doesn't apply to them. Take my word on this: Not only will you screw up equipment when you drop it, but you'll also quickly make enemies of the management who have to then bring in someone (at great cost) to get it repaired. This may come back to haunt you when you need advice from an experienced gym hand. And speaking of advice . . .
- *Don't* give it to your fellow trainees unless it's solicited, or unless you're absolutely certain the other person will hurt himself if he continues performing an exercise incorrectly. Chances are, this person is performing a variance of a movement (thousands exist) that you may not have seen yet.

21
Questions and Answers
(A Miniseminar with Lou)

It's doubtful that any professional bodybuilder competing today has given more seminars than I have. But I always enjoy hearing people's questions, as I often learn more from the query than they do from the answer. Questions cause you to think and reanalyze all of your training beliefs—to separate the wheat from the chaff. What follows first are some of the more commonly asked questions I receive at my seminars, and then several that I had John Little, senior writer at *FLEX* magazine, throw at me after reading over the manuscript that eventually became this book.

Bodybuilding Tips

Q: *What can a young girl expect from following your training system?*

A: A young girl—or anyone else, for that matter—will get out of it exactly what she puts into it, whether the goal is an increase in her present strength levels, her coordination, her general level of conditioning or firmness, or even therapeutic benefits. She, like anyone else, will have to make her own commitment, but she'll look and feel a whole lot better as a result.

Q: *Will I look like you when I've finished your program?*

A: That's a question that is impossible to answer. It will all depend on how hard you're willing to work and how consistently you're willing to train. I don't have an ironclad answer for you, but I do know that you'll certainly look a lot better than you do now.

Q: *I've been training three months, and I haven't made any gains. My friends have all shot past me in development. What am I doing wrong?*

A: First of all, you have to remember that everybody is different. You have a unique bone structure, metabolism, recovery ability, and innate adaptability to exercise. These and other components separate you from everybody else. Don't worry about comparisons. The only person you need to be concerned with is you, and you're the only person that any meaningful comparisons can be made against. Be patient; everybody responds at different rates of speed to bodybuilding.

Q: *I'm an older man, and I've never weight trained before. Should I work out two or three times a week?*

A: As a beginner, you should train body parts three times a week. Once you're an intermediate, you can train each body part twice a week, and eventually you can try the more advanced programs. Just ease into them gradually. Too much all at once will prove traumatic even to the most seasoned of athletes, let alone to someone who has never trained before. Slow and steady wins the race.

Q: *How can I reduce my waist while not losing any size anywhere else?*
A: Unfortunately, there's no such thing as spot reducing, so, what you ask is impossible. The body reduces its fat stores randomly—not in any one area. Be patient and persistent, and you'll find that you'll lose all the fat you want.

Q: *As a woman, will I get big and muscular if I follow your program?*
A: No, not at all. Women don't have enough of the male sex hormone testosterone in their bodies to develop big masculine muscles. You will, however, improve your shape and conditioning dramatically.

Q: *Is drinking water bad for me while I'm working out?*
A: No, it's no problem at all. If you want to drink water, go ahead—just don't drink *too* much.

Q: *How long should I rest between sets?*
A: A good trick is to wait until you catch your breath, then move on to your next set.

Q: *What nutrients do people who exercise need?*
A: You need protein, carbs, and fats—the macronutrients. Good nutrition consists of meat and fish for protein and building muscles; fruits and vegetables for fiber; and vitamins, minerals, and dairy products for bone growth and repair. We also need grains in our diets to provide additional vitamins and roughage.

Q: *How many vitamins should a beginner take?*
A: A person who is training regularly should definitely take a multivitamin/mineral supplement daily.

Q: *Can you tell me about sports-related injuries and how to avoid them, especially as you get older?*
A: Sports-related injuries are usually caused by a person's not getting enough rest, not eating properly, and not stretching sufficiently beforehand. If you continue to get adequate rest, a balanced diet, and sufficient warm-ups before training, you should be able to avoid all sports-related injuries.

Q: *How much fats should one have in a diet?*
A: The typical bodybuilder's diet should consist of all the macronutrients: fats, carbs, and protein. The percentage of fat in the diet should be in the neighborhood of 20 percent. Most Americans eat approximately 40 percent fat in their diets, and this is what leads to heart disease and high blood pressure.

Q: *At what time should I eat in relation to when I exercise?*
A: You should always space the time you eat from the time that you exercise. A good rule of thumb is not to eat at least one hour prior to the time you have scheduled to train. You should wait at least two hours after exercise to eat.

Q: *Will exercise make me hungrier?*
A: No, exercise will not make you more hungry. The reason for that is when you exercise, you burn fat, hopefully, and this produces ketones. Ketones are natural appetite suppressants. In other words, the more fat you burn, the less hungry you'll feel.

Q: *Can you tell me how to determine my target heart rate for aerobics?*
A: The safe level for a person to have, as far as heart rate is concerned, is based on a value known as the "target heart rate." This value

is obtained by subtracting your age from the number 220, and then multiplying that number by .75. This gives you the heart rate at which you can exercise and burn fat. If you have a heart rate below that, you won't be burning fat from your body, and if you go above that, aerobics won't be as effective a fat burner.

Q: *What do you do about muscle cramps?*
A: When you get a cramp, you should immediately stop exercising. Then stretch the muscle and gently massage it. Give yourself a rest. When the cramp goes away, you can then resume exercising at a slower pace.

Q: *What do you look for when you choose a professional gym?*
A: You have to be real careful when you're choosing a professional gym. Here is my personal checklist.

- Make sure the gym is conveniently located.
- The gym should have limited membership; check that the membership isn't too large for the facility, as you don't want to always have to wait in line to use the equipment.
- Your time should be quality time.
- The space should have the right atmosphere for your workout.
- The equipment should be properly maintained.
- The area should have good lighting and ventilation.
- Ample locker space should be provided.
- The facilities should be clean (including the showers).

Summing It All Up

John: *Lou, why did you write this book?*
Lou: I had two goals for this book. One was to set the record straight on *Pumping Iron.* I wanted to establish once and for all that the perception of me and my father sharing the dramatically supportive relationship as portrayed in the movie was and is a fraud. He was never supportive of me, and yet, despite this, I was able to persevere and succeed. It struck me that if I was able to be successful with all I've had to overcome, so can anyone else. Maybe there's another kid out there who is going through some tough problems. If I can reach him, and let him know that I didn't come from a charmed or privileged background either, it might make him think for himself and believe that he has worth as a person and not let go of his dreams.

Also, I've always wanted to write the most honest, thorough, and understanding book on bodybuilding and fitness for people of all ages. There's a lot of hype and B.S. out there with fad diets and exercise gadgets and machines that are next to worthless. The basics, however, never change. Unfortunately, with all of the media attention centered on bogus principles and equipment, many people overlook the sound traditional principles of basic bodybuilding. There's no easy way out.

John: *Let's back up a moment; what do you mean by saying that* Pumping Iron *was a fraud?*
Lou: Simply that so much of it was scripted; it wasn't the real documentary that everybody thought. And particularly the way it portrayed my "happy" family life; I was depressed and miserable through that entire period. As I mention in the book, my father actually wanted to kick me out of the house because I lost the Mr. Olympia contest.

John: *What do you think your father's reaction is going to be when he reads your book?*
Lou: Hard to say. The last time we spoke, it ended up with my hanging up on him, so I don't waste time these days worrying about how he will react to this or that. Again, the thrust of this book is that you

cannot exhaust your time and energy trying to change unchangeable situations or worrying about how other people perceive you. It's about believing in yourself and going out and doing what makes you happy—despite others' attempts to hold you down. I'll grant you that it's sad when you can't share your success and happiness with a parent, but, in my case at least, that just wasn't possible.

John: You recently ended a 17-year retirement and came back to compete in the Mr. Olympia contest at 40 years of age—and you brought the house down! Why the comeback?

Lou: Number one, I've always wanted to win the Mr. Olympia title, but, for one reason or another—usually show business commitments—I was never able to set aside the block of time necessary to train for it. The second thing is that I got tired of people in the gym saying, "Gee, Lou, it's too bad you're so old. It would have been great to see you compete for the title again." I took that as an insult. Sure, I was over 40 years of age, but I've never seen or considered that to be a "death sentence." I knew I was as strong at 41 as I ever was at 21 and that my physique had matured; the muscle on my body was thicker and denser, which only comes from years of persistent training. That's a plus. So I came back and wiped the floor with many competitors who were half my age and not quite so disrespectful afterward. Also, in coming back, I was able to fulfill the very real dreams I've had since I was in my 20s.

John: Then you came back again the next year—and placed even higher! Why was that if you'd proved your point with your comeback the year before?

Lou: Because while I'd proved my point to the doubting Thomases out there regarding how competitive we who are over 40 years old could be, I knew that I was far from

being in my best possible shape. I train only for me, just as I do everything else for me. It's always my decision, and my decisions impact my life favorably or negatively depending on how sincerely I hold the conviction. As a result, I knew I was in about 90 percent of the shape I could have been in, so I wanted to go out having given it my best possible shot, not a three-quarter effort. Plus, I wanted to show the world that life really does begin at 40!

John: When you say "I do everything else for me," are you including your wife and children in that sentence?

Lou: My wife, Carla, and my children, Shanna, Louie Jr., and Brent, mean everything to me. They're my world, my life, and my hope. However, my success in life has nothing at all to do with how much I love and respect my family. If it did, then I'd never have to work again because my love is that strong. Instead, my success—and I'm referring to earning money now—is contingent on my decisions and my ability to follow through on them. For example, my wife and I will discuss various movie roles I'm offered, and I'll generally follow Carla's recommendations—not because she's my wife, but because she has an excellent eye for such things, much better than my own in many ways. However, if I don't deliver a convincing performance on the screen, which is something I have to do on my own, then I don't get a second shot. In Hollywood, you're only as good as your most recent performance. So, yeah, in this respect, like training, it's up to me to do the best that I can possibly do. Everything else hinges on my success in doing that.

John: Is there one message you'd like to deliver to the people who read this book?

Lou: I want readers to know that life is too short for you not to pursue those goals that are dear to you. Don't let anyone tell you that you can't make it or that you're not worthy enough to even attempt it. Give it your best shot! I guarantee that if you don't try, you won't achieve your dreams—but if you do try, you're already halfway toward realizing them. If your family is behind you, God bless you, because it's going to be that much more enjoyable. However, if that isn't the case, then look at my example and dig in. Persevere. You can do it! You can be successful in whatever you want to be successful in. All you need is self-belief.

John: Isn't this a "Pollyanna platitude," a case of "believe and achieve"?

Lou: Well, I'm not sure I agree with the sentiment of "believe and achieve." I mean, if you honestly believe you're Napoleon, that only means you're insane, not that you're actually going to become the famed French military leader. However, you do have to "conceive" of something in order to "achieve" it. I conceived of a career in both bodybuilding and movies. Once I conceived it and envisioned it, then all that remained was looking for the most expedient way to "achieve" it, to make that conception a reality. In this regard, your mind most definitely is a driving, molding, and striving force for the attainment of your dreams, hopes, and desires. Self-confidence and persistence are the keys. Once you have these, and I think this book provides plenty of tips on how to obtain them, then nothing will stop you from achieving your goals.

Index

basic, 61–67
beginner's program, 68–70
for ectomorphs, 79–81
for endomorphs, 81–82
for mesomorphs, 82–84
warm-ups, 70–71

F

F vitamin, 93
Family's role, 53–56
Fat
gaining, 75, 77
losing, 95–97
Fat, in diet, 91–92, 176
Father
with Hodgkin's disease, 87–88
lack of encouragement, 25
and *Pumping Iron*, 25–26
reaction to bodybuilding, 13, 15
relationship with, 3–7
resistance to California move, 29–31
Ferrigno, Lou
athletics, in childhood, 9–10
beginning to work out, 10–11
childhood, 3–9
children in marriage, 55
chronology of life, xv–xvi
ear infections, 4
first home gym, 11
hearing loss, 5–6
Hercules training, 99–108
high school, 21
marriage to Carla Green, 55
poor nutrition, 87
working, in childhood, 28–29
Flat-bench dumbbell presses, 125
Flat-bench flyes, 124
FLEX magazine, 175
Fluorine, 93
Flyes, 74
Folic acid, 93
Forearm exercises, 157
basic, 85
Foreman, George, 43, 48

Front squats, 138

G

Girls, training for, 175
Goals
achieving, 37
in success formula, 35
Gold's Gym, 29
Grant, Bill, 12
Green, Carla, 53–55
Gyms
commercial, 172–173, 177
home, 169–173

H

Hack squats, 139
Hammer rows (seated rows), 130
Hamstring stretches, 71
Hearing aids, 6
Hearing loss, 5–6
Heavy training, by body type, 84–85
Heidenstam, Oscar, 22
Hercules, 17–19
Hercules, 99
training log for, 99–108
Heroes, 17–24
High school, 21
Hodgkin's disease, father with, 87–88
Holyfield, Evander, 43
Home gym, 169–173
equipment for, 13, 171–172
Homeostasis, 96
Hyperextensions, 132

I

Incline barbell presses, 123
Incline dumbbell curls, 148–149
The Incredible Hulk, 6
Injuries, 176
Inositol, 93
Instinctive training, 121
Intermediate routines

determination, 34
persistence, 34–35
self-belief, 33
short-term goals, 35
starting plan, 35–37
Sulfur, 94
Superhero fan, 6
Superstars competition, 59

T

Target heart rate, 176–177
Thiamine, 92
Thigh exercises, 136–137
    basic, 85
Training
    after 40, 39–43
    by body type, 79–85
    for *Hercules*, 99–108
    for muscular mass and strength, 73–77
Triceps exercises, 152–157
    basic, 85
Triceps pushdowns, 153
Twisting bent-knee sit-up, 67

V

Vanadium, 94
Vegetable proteins, 84
Visualization, 75
Vitamins, 84, 92–93, 176

W

Warm-up exercises, 70–71
Water
    in diet, 92
    drinking during training, 176
Weider, Joe, 11
    asked Lou to California, 28
    contract with, 29–31
Weight gain
    ectomorphs and, 79–81
    endomorphs and, 81–82
    mesomorphs and, 82–84
Weight lifting *vs.* bodybuilding, 171
Weight training, 59–60
Weissmuller, Johnny, 10
White Mountain Films, 25
Wide World of Sports, 27
Wide-grip pulldowns, 128–129
Women, muscle development, 176
Working, in childhood, 28–29
Wrist strips, 127

Y

Yates, Dorian, 39

Z

Zinc, 9